800 Questions
in
Calculus

From
Continental Mathematics League Contests
1981-2005

Skylight Publishing
Andover, Massachusetts

AP and Advanced Placement Program are registered trademarks of the College Entrance Examination Board, which was not involved in the production of and does not endorse this book.

Library of Congress Control Number: 2004096866

ISBN 0-9727055-4-6

Skylight Publishing
9 Bartlet Street, Suite 70
Andover, MA 01810

web: http://www.skylit.com
e-mail: sales@skylit.com
          support@skylit.com

1 2 3 4 5 6 7 8 9 10   08 07 06 05 04

Printed in the United States of America

Preface

The Continental Mathematics League has been bringing us fun competitions in mathematics and computer science since 1980. The annual calculus contest includes 32 questions, divided into four rounds. We are delighted to be able to offer you a book that brings together 800 questions from the past 25 years of CML calculus. The questions are presented in their original form with minor editing.

Actually, only 768 questions are included in the book: we weren't able to include the 32 questions from the 2005 contest because it was still in progress when the book went to print. Those 32 questions will appear at `http://www.skylit.com/calculus/cml` in April 2005.

The questions are arranged in order by year, starting from the most recent. The book also includes an index of questions by topic. Answers are included at the end of the book. Complete solutions are also available (see `http://www.skylit.com/calculus` for ordering information).

These questions offer a great opportunity to test your knowledge of calculus and practice for the AP exam. They stay within the range of the standard AP Calculus curriculum (mostly AB, but there are also a few questions on parametric curves, a BC topic). CML's philosophy is to emphasize wide participation rather than competitiveness. Therefore, most questions are of average difficulty. In each round, Questions 1-6 earn one point and Questions 7 and 8, perhaps slightly more challenging, earn two points. In this book, each year's questions are numbered from 1 to 32, so questions with numbers $8k-1$ and $8k$ ($k=1,2,3,4$) are two-pointers. They are marked with a ■.

This collection reflects the high school calculus tradition of the past 25 years. Many of the questions were written in the pre-calculus-reform and pre-calculator era. The collection includes a few calculator questions (which are marked with a ▤ icon). The rest of the questions are not "calculator-proof": calculator use may render them too easy or meaningless. Some questions may expect algebraic manipulation skills for which you haven't had enough practice. But none of it is insurmountable, and you can develop the necessary skills quickly. They will serve you well in the future.

Our sincere thanks to Joseph Quartararo, the president of the Continental Mathematics League, for organizing the contests and for making this unique collection of questions available for publication.

G. L.

$$A = \frac{bh}{2} = \frac{1}{2}ab\sin\theta \qquad A = \frac{(a+b)h}{2}$$

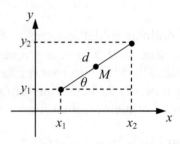

$$d = \sqrt{\left(x_2^2 - x_1^2\right) + \left(y_2^2 - y_1^2\right)}$$

$$\tan\theta = \frac{y_2 - y_1}{x_2 - x_1}$$

$$M = \left(\frac{x_1 + x_2}{2}, \frac{y_1 + y_2}{2}\right)$$

$$s = \theta r$$

$$A = \frac{\theta r^2}{2}$$

$$V = \frac{4}{3}\pi r^3$$

$$S.A. = 4\pi r^2$$

$$\sin^2 x + \cos^2 x = 1$$
$$1 + \tan^2 x = \sec^2 x$$
$$1 + \cot^2 x = \csc^2 x$$
$$\sin 2x = 2\sin x \cos x$$
$$\cos 2x = \cos^2 x - \sin^2 x$$
$$= 2\cos^2 x - 1$$
$$= 1 - 2\sin^2 x$$

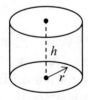

$$V = \pi r^2 h$$
$$S.A. = 2\pi r^2 + 2\pi rh$$

$$V = \frac{1}{3}\pi r^2 h$$

Contents

2004

1. The $\lim_{x \to 4} \dfrac{4-x}{\sqrt{x}-2} =$

    (A) $-\infty$ (B) -4 (C) 0 (D) 4 (E) ∞

2.

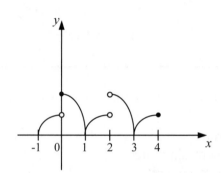

The function shown above is defined on the closed interval $-1 \le x \le 4$ for

(A) all x (B) all x except $x = 0$
(C) all x except $x = 1$ (D) all x except $x = 2$
(E) all x except $x = 0$ and $x = 2$

3.

x	-8	-6	-4	-2	0	2	4
$f(x)$	0	5	0	-2	-4	-6	-4
$f'(x)$	4	0	-4	-2	-1	0	1
$f''(x)$	-2	-6	-2	0	1	4	3

For some key values of x, the values of $f(x)$, $f'(x)$ and $f''(x)$ are given in the table above. The equation of the tangent to the curve $y = f(x)$ at the point of inflection shown in the table is:

(A) $y = 4x$ (B) $y = 4x + 8$
(C) $y = -6x + 24$ (D) $y = -2x - 6$ (E) $y = -x + 3$

4.   Using the table in the previous problem, at $x = -8$ the function $y = f(x)$ is

(A)   at a relative minimum
(B)   increasing at an increasing rate
(C)   increasing at a decreasing rate
(D)   decreasing at an increasing rate
(E)   decreasing at a decreasing rate

5.   The graph of the function $f(x) = \dfrac{\left| x^3 \right|}{x^3 - 8}$ has the following asymptotes:

(A)   one vertical and one horizontal
(B)   two vertical and one horizontal
(C)   one vertical and two horizontal
(D)   three vertical and one horizontal
(E)   two vertical and two horizontal

6.   Find the limit as $a \to 0$ of the y-intercept of the normal to the parabola $y = x^2$ at the point $\left(a,\ a^2 \right)$.

7.■   Let $f(x) = \begin{cases} bx^2 + 6x, & \text{if } x \le 2 \\ ax^3, & \text{if } x > 2 \end{cases}$. Find the values of a and b such that $f(x)$ is differentiable at $x = 2$.

8.▪ Determine the constants a, b, c, and d so that the graph of $y = ax^3 + bx^2 + cx + d$ has a relative maximum at $(2, 4)$ and a point of inflection at the origin.

---

9. The function $f(x)$ is continuous on the closed interval $[-3, 5]$ and differentiable on the open interval $(-3, 5)$. If $f'(x) > 0$ over the interval and if $f(-3) = -4$ and $f(5) = 12$, then $f(-1)$ cannot equal

(A) −6   (B) −1   (C) 4   (D) 5   (E) 10

---

10. Let $f(x) = \begin{cases} \dfrac{x^3 + 8}{x + 2} & \text{, if } x \neq -2 \\ 4 & \text{, if } x = -2 \end{cases}$. Which of the following four statements are true?

    I. $f(x)$ is defined at $x = -2$
    II. $f(x)$ is continuous at $x = -2$
    III. $\lim\limits_{x \to -2} f(x)$ exists
    IV. $f(x)$ is differentiable at $x = -2$

(A) I only   (B) I and II   (C) I and III
(D) II and III   (E) I, II, III and IV

---

11. For which of the following functions $f(x)$ do $f(0)$ and $f'(0)$ exist, but not $f''(0)$?

(A) $f(x) = x^{-\frac{1}{2}}$ (B) $f(x) = x^{\frac{1}{3}}$ (C) $f(x) = x^{\frac{4}{3}}$

(D) $f(x) = x^{\frac{7}{2}}$ (E) $f(x) = x^{\frac{11}{5}}$

---

12. For a right circular cylinder with radius r and height h, volume $V = \pi r^2 h$ and surface area $S = 2\pi r^2 + 2\pi rh$. If the radius is a function of time and the height of the cylinder is equal to the diameter, then $\dfrac{dV}{dt} =$

(A) $r\dfrac{dS}{dt}$ (B) $2r\dfrac{dS}{dt}$ (C) $\dfrac{r}{2}\dfrac{dS}{dt}$ (D) $\dfrac{1}{r}\dfrac{dS}{dt}$ (E) $\dfrac{1}{r^2}\dfrac{dS}{dt}$

13.

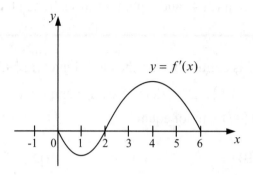

$y = f'(x)$

The graph of $f'(x)$ is shown above. For which of the following values of x is $f(x)$ concave down?

(A) $x = \dfrac{1}{2}$ (B) $x = \dfrac{3}{2}$ (C) $x = 2$ (D) $x = \dfrac{5}{2}$ (E) $x = 3$

---

14.   Find the coordinates of the point where the line tangent to the parabola $y^2 = 8x$ at $(2, 4)$ intersects the axis of symmetry of the parabola.

15.■   The acceleration of a particle is given by $a(t) = 36t^2 - 12$ and $s(t)$ is the position function. If $s(-1) = -2$ and $s(2) = 37$, find the velocity of the particle at $t = 1$.

16.■   Chord $\overline{AB}$ of the parabola $y = x^2$ moves up from the vertex at $\dfrac{3}{4}$ units/sec, always remaining parallel to the x-axis. Triangle ABC is formed by $\overline{AB}$ and the two tangents to the parabola at A and at B. The triangle increases in area as $\overline{AB}$ moves up. Find the rate at which the area is increasing in units²/sec at the instant when $\overline{AB}$ is 4 units above the vertex.

17.

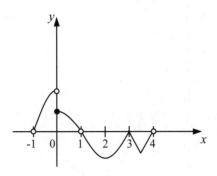

The function, shown above, is differentiable at

(A) $x = 1$ (B) $x = 2$ (C) $x = 3$ (D) $x = 2$ and $x = 3$
(E) $x = 0$, $x = 3$, and $x = 4$

18.   If $p > 0$ and $q > 0$, $\int_p^{p+q} \dfrac{dx}{x^2} =$

(A) q (B) $\dfrac{p+q}{p}$ (C) $\dfrac{p}{p+q}$ (D) $\dfrac{q-p}{pq}$ (E) $\dfrac{q}{p(p+q)}$

19.   If $h(x) = 2f^2(x) - 3g^2(x)$, $f'(x) = g(x)$, and $g'(x) = -f(x)$, then $h'(x) =$

(A) $-10f(x)g(x)$ (B) $-2f(x)g(x)$
(C) $2f(x)g(x)$ (D) $10f(x)g(x)$
(E) $2f'(x)g'(x)$

20.   If $x > 0$ and $n > 1$, then the area bounded by the curves $y = x^n$ and $y = \sqrt[n]{x}$ is

(A) 1   (B) $n-1$ (C) $n+1$ (D) $\dfrac{n-1}{n+1}$ (E) $\dfrac{n+1}{n-1}$

21.

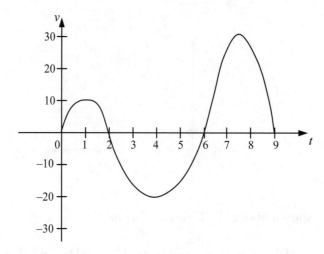

The graph of the velocity of a particle traveling along the x-axis for $0 \le t \le 9$ is shown above. At $t = 0$, $x = 0$. Approximately how many units to the right of the origin is the position of the particle at $t = 9$?

(A) 2   (B) 8   (C) 15   (D) 27   (E) 31

---

22. Given the curve $y^2 = 150 - 10x$, $0 \le x \le 15$, find the coordinates of the point on the curve in the first quadrant that is nearest the origin.

23.■ The curve $y = \dfrac{ax + b}{(x-4)(x-1)}$ has a relative maximum at the point $(2, -1)$. Find a and b.

24.■ The average value of the function $f(x) = ax^2 - 2ax + a$ over the interval $[1, 4]$ equals 13. Find the value of a.

25. If the function $f(x)$ is such that $f(1) = 4$, $f(2) = 4$, and $f''(x)$ exists and is positive on the closed interval [0, 4], then we must have

    (A) $f'(1.5) = 0$ (B) $f'(1.5) > 0$
    (C) $f'(3) > 0$ (D) $f'(3) < 0$
    (E) none of the above

26. Find the range of $y = \dfrac{e}{x^2 - \pi^2}$ in terms of e and π.

27. If $f(x) = e^x$, $g(x) = \sin x$, and $h(x) = f(g(x))$, then $h'\left(\dfrac{\pi}{2}\right) =$

    (A) -1 (B) 0 (C) $e^{-\frac{\pi}{2}}$ (D) 1 (E) $e^{\frac{\pi}{2}}$

28. If $f'(x) = 6x^2$ and $f(2) = 1$, then $\displaystyle\int_0^2 f(x)\,dx =$

    (A) -22 (B) -16 (C) 2 (D) 8 (E) 18

29. The expression $e^1 + e^2 + e^3$ is a

    (A) left-hand Riemann sum with 3 subintervals for $\displaystyle\int_0^4 e^x\,dx$

    (B) left-hand Riemann sum with 3 subintervals for $\displaystyle\int_0^3 e^x\,dx$

    (C) right-hand Riemann sum with 3 subintervals for $\displaystyle\int_0^3 e^x\,dx$

    (D) right-hand Riemann sum with 3 subintervals for $\displaystyle\int_1^4 e^x\,dx$

    (E) midpoint Riemann sum with 4 subintervals for $\displaystyle\int_0^4 e^x\,dx$

30. The rate of growth of an investment, which is compounded continuously, is proportional to the current balance with the constant of proportionality being the rate of interest. How much money (to the nearest dollar) should a 20-year-old person invest at $9\frac{1}{2}\%$ annual interest compounded continuously to have half a million dollars at age 70?

(A) $433   (B) $1,336   (C) $4,326   (D) $8,756   (E) $23,781

31.■ The area in the first quadrant bounded above by $y = \sin x$, below by the x-axis, and to the right by $x = \dfrac{\pi}{2}$ is divided into two equal parts by the line $x = a$. Find a.

32.■ The base of a solid is the region in the first quadrant bounded by the ellipse $\dfrac{x^2}{9} + \dfrac{y^2}{4} = 1$. Each cross-section perpendicular to the x-axis is an isosceles right triangle with a leg as the base. Find the volume of the solid.

2003

1. $\displaystyle\lim_{x \to \pi} \frac{\pi x - \pi^2}{2x - 2\pi} =$

(A) 0   (B) $\dfrac{\pi}{2}$ (C) π (D) 2π (E) ∞

---

2. The equation for the horizontal asymptote for the function
$$f(x) = \frac{(2x-5)(3x+6)(x+1)^4}{(x-9)^6} \text{ is}$$

(A) $y = 0$ (B) $y = 1$ (C) $y = 4$ (D) $y = 6$ (E) $y = 10$

---

3. The conditions necessary to apply Rolle's Theorem are: 1) f is continuous on $[a, b]$; 2) f is differentiable on (a, b); and 3) $f(a) = f(b)$.

Which one of the following functions does NOT satisfy at least one of the above conditions?

(A) $f(x) = x^3 - x$ on $[0, 1]$

(B) $f(x) = \sqrt{8 - x^3}$ on $[-2, 2]$

(C) $f(x) = x^{\frac{4}{3}} - 1$ on $[-1, 1]$

(D) $f(x) = \dfrac{x^2 - 4}{x - 3}$ on $[-2, 2]$

(E) $f(x) = x^2 - 4x$ on $[0, 4]$

---

4. The function $f(x) = x^3 - 4x^2 + 9x - 5$ in the vicinity of the point $(1, 1)$ is

(A) increasing at a decreasing rate
(B) increasing at an increasing rate
(C) decreasing at a decreasing rate
(D) decreasing at an increasing rate
(E) neither increasing nor decreasing

5. The line $y = 4x + 13$ is tangent to the curve $y = -2x^2 + kx + 5$, where $k < 0$. Find k.

6. Let $f(x) = \begin{cases} x + 2a, & \text{if } x < 1 \\ ax^2 + 7x - 4, & \text{if } x \geq 1 \end{cases}$. If a is such that $f(x)$ is continuous at $x = 1$, is $f(x)$ also differentiable at $x = 1$? Justify your answer.

7.■

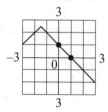

Given the graph of $f(x)$ above, sketch a graph of $f'(x)$ for $-2\frac{1}{2} \leq x \leq 2\frac{1}{2}$.

8.■ Determine the coefficient c so that the curve $f(x) = ax^3 + bx^2 + cx + d$ has a relative minimum at $(2, -10)$ and a point of inflection at $(0, 6)$.

9. Recall that $1^3 + 2^3 + ... + n^3 = \dfrac{n^2(n+1)^2}{4}$. Find $\lim\limits_{n \to \infty} \dfrac{1^3 + 2^3 + ... + n^3}{\dfrac{1}{2}n^4 - 3n^3 + n^2}$.

10. The coordinates of the point where the normal to the curve $y = \dfrac{1}{3}x^3 + \dfrac{1}{2}x^2 + x$ at $x = 1$ intersects the y-axis are

(A) $\left(0, \dfrac{3}{2}\right)$ (B) $\left(\dfrac{3}{2}, 0\right)$ (C) $\left(0, \dfrac{13}{6}\right)$ (D) $\left(\dfrac{13}{6}, 0\right)$ (E) $\left(0, \dfrac{5}{3}\right)$

11. $3x^2$ and $3x^3$ are both increasing and positive for $x > 0$. How many times greater is the rate of increase of $3x^3$ than the rate of increase of $3x^2$ at $x = 4$?

(A) 2   (B) 4   (C) 6   (D) 8   (E) 16

12.

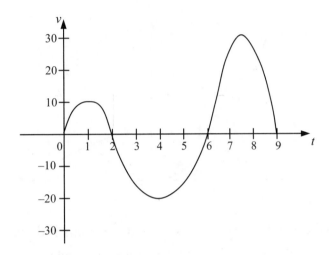

The graph of the velocity of a particle moving along the x-axis for $0 \le t \le 9$ is shown above. At $t = 0$, $x = 0$. At which time is the particle furthest to the left of the origin?

(A) $t = 0$ (B) $t = 2$ (C) $t = 4$ (D) $t = 6$ (E) $t = 9$

13. $y = x - \dfrac{k}{a^2}x^2$, $k > 0$. If a is doubled, then the maximum height of the curve

(A) remains the same
(B) is increased by a factor of 2
(C) is decreased by a factor of 2
(D) is increased by a factor of 4
(E) is decreased by a factor of 4

14. Let f and g be differentiable functions, where $f(2) = 6$, $g(2) = 4$, $f'(2) = -5$, $g'(2) = -2$, $f'(4) = -3$, $g'(4) = 3$. If $h(x) = f\big(g(x)\big)$, then $h'(2) =$

(A) -20 (B) -12 (C) -6 (D) -3 (E) 6

15. ■

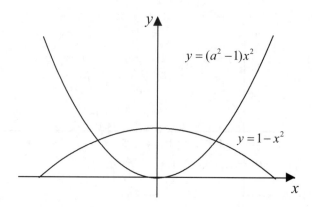

The region between the curve $y = 1 - x^2$ and the x-axis is divided into 4 equal parts by the y-axis and the curve $y = (a^2 - 1)x^2$ ($a > 1$). Find the value of a.

16. ■

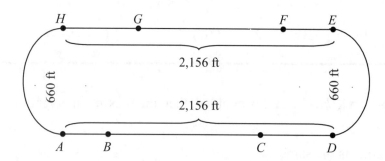

A racecar driver intends to race around the track in the following manner: on the curves from D to E and H to A he will drive with a constant velocity of 132 ft/sec; from A to B and E to F, he will accelerate at 22 ft/sec² up to a velocity of 176 ft/sec; he will maintain that velocity from B to C and F to G. He will then decelerate at 11 ft/sec² so that his velocity at D and H is 132 ft/sec. AD and EH are each 2,156 ft long, and DE and HA are each 660 ft long. How many seconds will it take the car to go once around the track?

17. $\lim\limits_{h \to 0} \dfrac{e^{4+h} - e^4}{h} =$

(A) e^3 (B) e^4 (C) $4e^3$ (D) $4e^4$ (E) $5e^5$

18. For $-2\pi \le x \le 2\pi$ the line $y = \dfrac{1}{2}$ intersects the curve $y = \sin|x|$ only when $x =$

(A) $\dfrac{-5\pi}{6}, \dfrac{-\pi}{6}, \dfrac{\pi}{6}, \dfrac{5\pi}{6}$ (B) $\dfrac{-5\pi}{6}, \dfrac{-\pi}{6}, \dfrac{7\pi}{6}, \dfrac{11\pi}{6}$

(C) $\dfrac{-11\pi}{6}, \dfrac{-7\pi}{6}, \dfrac{\pi}{6}, \dfrac{5\pi}{6}$ (D) $\dfrac{-11\pi}{6}, \dfrac{-7\pi}{6}, \dfrac{7\pi}{6}, \dfrac{11\pi}{6}$

(E) $\dfrac{-11\pi}{6}, \dfrac{-7\pi}{6}, \dfrac{-5\pi}{6}, \dfrac{-\pi}{6}, \dfrac{\pi}{6}, \dfrac{5\pi}{6}, \dfrac{7\pi}{6}, \dfrac{11\pi}{6}$

19. If $f(x)$ is an odd function, $\displaystyle\int_0^3 f(x)\,dx = 8$, and $\displaystyle\int_2^3 f(x)\,dx = 2$, then $\displaystyle\int_{-2}^0 f(x)\,dx =$

(A) -10 (B) -6 (C) 0 (D) 6 (E) 10

20.

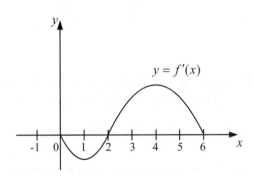

The graph of $f'(x)$ is shown above. On the interval $0 \le x \le 6$, for what value of x does $f(x)$ achieve its absolute maximum value?

(A) $x = 0$ (B) $x = 2$ (C) $x = 4$ (D) $x = 6$
(E) cannot be determined

21. Find the value of c which satisfies Rolle's Theorem for the function
$f(x) = \sin(x^2)$ on $\left[0, \sqrt{\pi}\right]$.

22. The function $y = \sin\left(\dfrac{\pi}{x}\right)$ has infinite number of relative maxima and relative minima. Which of the following values of x does NOT yield a relative maximum or minimum?

   (A) $\dfrac{2}{7}$ (B) $\dfrac{2}{5}$ (C) $\dfrac{2}{3}$ (D) $\dfrac{3}{2}$ (E) 2

23. ■

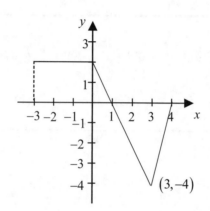

The graph of the function f, shown above, consists of a horizontal segment and segments of lines $y = -2x + 2$ and $y = 4x - 16$. Let g be given by

$g(x) = \displaystyle\int_0^x f(t)\,dt$. Write an equation of the line tangent to the graph of g at $x = 3$.

24. ■ The force F (in pounds) of water resistance on a boat with speed v (in ft/sec) is given by the formula $F = -kv^2$. The constant k is called the *drag coefficient*. The force F equals mass times acceleration $F = ma = m\dfrac{dv}{dt} = -kv^2$. The mass m is the weight divided by 32, $m = \dfrac{w}{32}$. A certain boat is coasting with sails down. The only force acting on it is water resistance. It takes the boat 25 seconds to slow down from a speed of 8 ft/sec to a speed of 4 ft/sec. The boat weighs 6,720 pounds. What is the drag coefficient of this boat? Give your answer accurate to two decimal places.

25. $\int x^2 e^{x^3}\, dx =$

    (A) $\dfrac{e^{x^3}}{3}+C$ (B) $\dfrac{2xe^{x^3}}{3}+C$

    (C) $2xe^{x^3}+C$ (D) $3x^4 e^{x^3}+C$

    (E) none of the above

26. If $y = 3\sin x + 4\cos x$, then $y'' - y =$

    (A) $-6\sin x - 8\cos x$ (B) $-6\sin x + 8\cos x$

    (C) $6\sin x - 8\cos x$ (D) $6\sin x + 8\cos x$

    (E) 0

27.

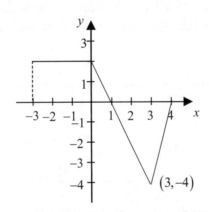

The graph of the function f consists of a horizontal segment and segments of lines $y = -2x + 2$ and $y = 4x - 16$. Let g be given by $g(x) = \int_0^x f(t)\, dt$. For what value of x in the interval $-3 < x < 3$ does g have a relative maximum?

28. For the function g defined in the previous question, find $g(4)$.

29. The expression $f(1)+f(2)+f(3)$ is a right-hand Riemann sum for $y=f(x)$ on the interval $[0, 3]$ with 3 subintervals. The same expression would represent

    (A)   the left-hand Riemann sum on $[1, 4]$ with 3 subintervals
    (B)   the left-hand Riemann sum on $[0, 3]$ with 3 subintervals
    (C)   the right-hand Riemann sum on $[0, 3]$ with 4 subintervals
    (D)   the right-hand Riemann sum on $[1, 4]$ with 3 subintervals
    (E)   the midpoint Riemann sum on $[0, 4]$ with 4 subintervals

30. Recall that $\int \ln x\, dx = x\ln x - x + C$. Find the area of the region in the first quadrant bounded by the graph of $y = \ln x$, the line tangent to $y = \ln x$ at $x = 3$, and the x- and y-axes.

31.■ An object is projected out horizontally with a velocity of 960 ft/sec from the top of a building 160 ft high. How far from the base of the building will the object land? (Assume the acceleration due to gravity $g = -32$ ft/sec^2. Hint: $v_x = 960$ ft/sec. Find v_y.)

32.■

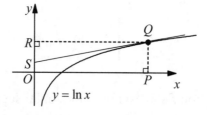

The line SQ is tangent to the curve $y = \ln x$ at the point Q. The area of trapezoid $OPQS$ is 3 times the area of triangle QRS. ($\overline{QR}$ is perpendicular to the y-axis.) Find the coordinates of Q.

2002

1. $\lim\limits_{x \to 0} \dfrac{x^5 - 16x}{x^3 - 4x} =$

    (A) −4   (B) −2   (C) 0   (D) 2   (E) 4

---

2. The sum of two non-negative numbers is 6. If the square of one of the numbers is multiplied by the second number, then the largest possible product is

    (A) 32   (B) 36   (C) 38   (D) 45   (E) 64

---

3. The minimum value of the function $y = \sqrt{x^2 + 2ax + 10a^2}$, where $a > 0$, is

    (A) −a   (B) a   (C) 3a   (D) 6a   (E) $9a^2$

---

4. The average value of the function $y = x - \dfrac{k}{a^2}x^2$ on the interval between its

    x-intercepts is

    (A) $\dfrac{k}{2a^2}$ (B) $\dfrac{k}{a^2}$ (C) $\dfrac{a^2}{6k}$ (D) $\dfrac{a^4}{6k^2}$ (E) $\dfrac{2a^4}{3k^2}$

5.

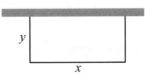

    A farmer needs to fence in a rectangular region shown above. Since one side is along a river, fencing is needed only for three sides. What should be the ratio of x to y to maximize the area of the enclosed region for the given total length of the fence?

    (A) 1:1   (B) $\sqrt{2}$:1   (C) $\sqrt{3}$:1   (D) 2:1   (E) 3:1

6.   A function f is defined for all real numbers and has the following property: for any a, $f(x+a)-f(x)=3x^2a-9a^2$. Find $f'(-4)$.

7. ■

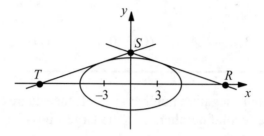

The figure above shows the ellipse $\dfrac{x^2}{25}+\dfrac{y^2}{9}=1$ with the tangents to it at $x=3$ and $x=-3$ in the first and second quadrants. Find the area of the triangle $\triangle RST$ with the vertices at the x-intercepts, R and T, and the y-intercept, S.

8. ■   A manufacturer makes a number of cloth dolls C and a number of plastic dolls P each month, where $P=\dfrac{108-C}{C}$. The selling price of a cloth doll is three times the selling price of a plastic doll. Find the total number of dolls that should be made each month to maximize the amount of money received from sales.

9. $\displaystyle\lim_{x\to\infty}\dfrac{3x^5-4}{x-2x^5}=$

     (A) $-\dfrac{3}{2}$ (B) -1 (C) 0 (D) 1 (E) $\dfrac{3}{2}$

10.   The area in the first quadrant bounded by the curve $y=\sqrt{9-x}$ and the x- and y-axes is

     (A)   9   (B)   18   (C)   27   (D)   35   (E) $40\dfrac{1}{2}$

11. Find the coordinates of the point on the curve $xy = 10$ in the first quadrant such that the normal to the curve passes through the origin.

12. If $f'(x)$ exists for all x and $f(1) = 10$ and $f(8) = -4$, then, for at least one value of c in the open interval $(1, 8)$, which of the following must be true?

   (A) $f(c) = 12$ (B) $f(c) = -12$ (C) $f'(c) = 2$
   (D) $f'(c) = -2$ (E) $f(c^2) = 16$

13. What is the value of k such that the curve $y = x^3 - \dfrac{k}{x}$ has a point of inflection at $x = 1$?

   (A) $k = 2$ (B) $k = -2$ (C) $k = 3$ (D) $k = -3$
   (E) none of the above

14. A particle moves along the x-axis starting at the origin at $t = 0$. Its acceleration at any time t is $a(t) = -6t$. Find the velocity of the particle at $t = 0$, if the maximum displacement of the particle in the positive direction is 16 units.

15.■ $\dfrac{1}{z} = \dfrac{1}{x} + \dfrac{1}{y}$. If x is increasing at 4 units/sec and y is increasing at 6 units/sec, how fast is z increasing when $x = 20$ and $y = 30$?

16.■ A baker is baking a circular pie. He wants to cut out a slice (a sector) with a perimeter $2r + s = 38$ inches. He would like the area A_s of the slice to be as large as possible. What should the radius of the pie be? (Recall that $\dfrac{A_s}{\pi r^2} = \dfrac{s}{2\pi r}$.)

17. $\displaystyle\lim_{x \to 0} \frac{e^{2x} - 1}{e^x - 1} =$

   (A) 0   (B) 1   (C) 2   (D) e^x (E) ∞

18. Suppose $f(x)$ is an even function, $\int_{-3}^{3} f(x)\,dx = 10$, and $\int_{3}^{5} f(x)\,dx = 2$. Find $\int_{0}^{5} f(x)\,dx$.

19. If $f(x) = x \ln x$, $x > 0$, then $f'(x) < 0$ when

(A) $0 < x < \dfrac{1}{e}$ (B) $\dfrac{1}{e} < x < 1$ (C) $1 < x < e$ (D) $x > 0$ (E) $x > e$

20. $\displaystyle \lim_{h \to 0} \frac{e^{x+h} - e^{x-h}}{h} =$

(A) 0 (B) e^x (C) $2e^x$ (D) e^{2x} (E) ∞

21. ▣ Find a positive value of x that satisfies the Mean Value Theorem for $f(x) = \sin x$ on the closed interval $\left[-\dfrac{3\pi}{2}, \dfrac{3\pi}{2} \right]$.

22. ▣ If $\displaystyle \int_{1}^{2} (4 + \ln x)\,dx$ is approximated by a midpoint Riemann sum with four subintervals of equal length, then the value is

(A) 4.297 (B) 4.388 (C) 4.470 (D) 4.514 (E) 4.669

23. ▪ A car accelerates from rest at a rate of 2 meters/sec². Then the brake is applied and the car decelerates at a rate of 4 meters/sec² until it stops. The total travel time is 12 seconds. What is the total travel distance?

24.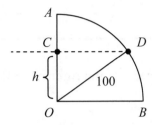

Arc AB is $\frac{1}{4}$ of a circle with radius $r = 100$. Particle C falls vertically from point A towards O. Its height (above O) is given by $h = 100 - 16t^2$. The particle is projected horizontally onto the arc, so that its shadow D moves along the arc. How many seconds after the particle starts moving is the speed of the shadow twice the speed of the particle?

25. $\lim\limits_{x \to 10^9} \tan\left(\dfrac{4x\pi - \pi}{4}\right) =$

(A) -1 (B) 0 (C) 1 (D) $\sqrt{3}$ (E) ∞

26. Find $\displaystyle\int \dfrac{dx}{\sqrt[3]{(b + ax)^2}}$.

27. If $g(x) = x^2$, $y = f\big(g(x)\big)$, and $f'(x) = \sqrt{5x - 1}$, then $\dfrac{dy}{dx} =$

(A) $2x\sqrt{5x^2 - 1}$ (B) $\dfrac{5x}{\sqrt{5x - 1}}$ (C) $\dfrac{5x}{\sqrt{5x^2 - 1}}$

(D) $x^2\sqrt{5x - 1}$ (E) $\dfrac{x^2}{2\sqrt{5x - 1}}$

28. If $y = \sin x + e^{-x}$, then $y + y'' =$

(A) 0 (B) $2\sin x$ (C) $2e^{-x}$

(D) $2\sin x + 2e^{-x}$ (E) $2\sin x - 2e^{-x}$

29. Find the minimum value of $y = \dfrac{e^x - e^{-x}}{2} + \dfrac{5}{4}\dfrac{e^x + e^{-x}}{2}$.

30. Which of the following represents the right-hand Riemann sum for $\displaystyle\int_0^\pi \sin x\, dx$ with four subintervals of equal length?

(A) $\dfrac{1}{4}\left(\sin\dfrac{\pi}{4} + \sin\dfrac{\pi}{2} + \sin\dfrac{3\pi}{4} + \sin\pi\right)$

(B) $\dfrac{1}{4}\left(\sin 0 + \sin\dfrac{\pi}{4} + \sin\dfrac{\pi}{2} + \sin\dfrac{3\pi}{4}\right)$

(C) $\dfrac{\pi}{4}\left(\sin 0 + \sin\dfrac{\pi}{4} + \sin\dfrac{\pi}{2} + \sin\dfrac{3\pi}{4}\right)$

(D) $\dfrac{\pi}{4}\left(\sin\dfrac{\pi}{4} + \sin\dfrac{\pi}{2} + \sin\dfrac{3\pi}{4} + \sin\pi\right)$

(E) $\dfrac{1}{5}\left(\sin 0 + \sin\dfrac{\pi}{4} + \sin\dfrac{\pi}{2} + \sin\dfrac{3\pi}{4} + \sin\pi\right)$

31.■▣
    Find the volume of the solid formed by revolving the region bounded by the curves $y = e^{-x}$, $y = \ln x$, and $x = 1$ about the y-axis.

32.■ If an object weighs 81 pounds at the surface of Earth, then its weight w in pounds at any height h, measured in miles, above the surface of Earth, is

$$w = 81\left(1 + \frac{h}{4000}\right)^{-2} = 81\left(\frac{4000}{4000 + h}\right)^2.$$ The weight decreases as the height increases.

If the object is propelled directly upward at a constant speed of 18 miles per second, then at what rate, in pounds per second, is the weight decreasing at the moment when the object's weight is 64 pounds?

2001

1. $\lim\limits_{x\to\infty}\dfrac{\sqrt{x}+\sqrt[3]{8x}+4}{\sqrt{4x}+\sqrt[3]{x}+4}=$

   (A) $\dfrac{1}{2}$ (B) 1   (C) $\dfrac{3}{2}$ (D) 2   (E) $\dfrac{5}{2}$

---

2. If $f(x)=\left(4x^3-4\right)\left(\sqrt{x}-2\right)$, then $f'(1)=$

   (A) -12 (B) $-11\dfrac{1}{2}$ (C) 0   (D) 1   (E) $11\dfrac{1}{2}$

---

3. An object is thrown vertically into the air. Its height in feet at any time t is given by $h(t)=-16t^2+48t+5$. How high does the object rise?

   (A) 37 ft   (B) 41 ft   (C) 48 ft   (D) 53 ft   (E) 113 ft

---

4. If $f(x)=|x|$, then $f'(-2)=$

   (A) -2 (B) -1 (C) 0   (D) 1   (E) 2

---

5. Let $C(x)$ represent the total cost (in dollars) of producing a quantity x of some product. The marginal cost $M(x)=C'(x)$ is the derivative of the total cost function. The average cost $A(x)=\dfrac{C(x)}{x}$. If $C(x)=10x^2-48x+8000$, then find the difference between the average cost and marginal cost at $x=25$.

---

6. If $f(x) = \dfrac{1}{(1-x)^2}$, then the n-th derivative of $f(x)$ is

(A) $\dfrac{n!}{(1-x)^n}$ (B) $\dfrac{(n+1)!}{(1-x)^{n+1}}$ (C) $\dfrac{(n+1)!}{(1-x)^{n+2}}$

(D) $\dfrac{(-1)^n(n+1)!}{(1-x)^{n+2}}$ (E) $\dfrac{(-1)^{n+1}(n+1)!}{(1-x)^{n+1}}$

7.■ $f(x) = \begin{cases} bx^3 + 7, & \text{if } x < 3 \\ ax^2 + 3, & \text{if } x \geq 3 \end{cases}$. Find the values of a and b such that $f(x)$ is differentiable at $x = 3$.

8.■ Three tangent lines can be drawn to the curve $y = x^3 + 4x^2$ from the point $(1, -4)$. The sum of the slopes of these three tangent lines is

(A) $-\dfrac{1}{2}$ (B) $\dfrac{1}{2}$ (C) $15\dfrac{1}{2}$ (D) $20\dfrac{3}{4}$ (E) $28\dfrac{1}{4}$

9. $\lim\limits_{h \to 0} \dfrac{8\sqrt{16+h} - 32}{h} =$

(A) -1 (B) $-\dfrac{1}{2}$ (C) $\dfrac{1}{2}$ (D) 1 (E) 4

10. If $x^4 - 3x^2 y^2 + 4y^2 = 5$, then the value of $\dfrac{dy}{dx}$ at $(1, 2)$ is

(A) -1 (B) 1 (C) 3 (D) 5 (E) undefined

11. A particle moves along the x-axis with acceleration $a(t) = 6t - 4$ units^2/sec. Given that $x = 10$ when $t = 1$ and $x = 30$ when $t = 3$, find the velocity of the particle at $t = 2$.

12. The function $f(x) = 4\sqrt[3]{x^2} - 4$ does not satisfy Rolle's Theorem on the interval $[-1, 1]$ because

   (A) $f(0) \neq 0$
   (B) $f(1) = f(-1)$
   (C) $f(x)$ is not continuous on $[-1, 1]$
   (D) $f(2) > f(1)$
   (E) $f(x)$ is not differentiable on $(1, -1)$

13. The derivative of the composite function $f(g(x))$ is

   (A) $f(x)f'(x)g'(x)$ (B) $f(g'(x))f'(x)$
   (C) $f'(x)g'(x)$ (D) $f'(g(x))g'(x)$
   (E) $f'(g'(x))$

14. If $\int_{-2}^{4} f(x)\,dx = 3$ and $\int_{-2}^{6} f(x)\,dx = 1$, then $\int_{4}^{6} [f(x) + 5]\,dx =$

   (A) -2 (B) 0   (C) 5   (D) 8   (E) 12

15. ▪ Two tangent lines can be drawn from the origin to the curve $y = x^2 + 4$. Find the area of the triangle formed by these two tangent lines and the line segment joining the points of tangency.

16. ▪ The illumination from a bulb varies directly with the intensity of the light and inversely with the square of the distance from the source. Two bulbs are placed 35 feet apart. The intensity of bulb K is 27 cd and the intensity of bulb L is 64 cd. What is the distance from bulb K to the darkest point along the line connecting the two bulbs?

17. The curve $3y^2 - 3xy + 2x^3 = 7$ has vertical tangents when

   (A) $x = y$ (B) $2x = y$ (C) $x = 2y$ (D) $3x = y$ (E) $x = 3y$

18. If $\int_3^5 f(x)\,dx = k$, then $\int_3^5 f(x)\,dx - \int_3^1 f(x+2)\,dx =$

(A) $-2k$ (B) $-k$ (C) 0 (D) k (E) $2k$

---

19. $\int (x-4)\,dx =$

(A) $\dfrac{x^2}{2} - 4x + C$ (B) $\dfrac{x^3}{3} - \dfrac{3x^2}{2} - 4x + C$

(C) $\dfrac{x^2}{3} - 2x^2 - 3x + C$ (D) $\dfrac{x^3}{3} - 2x^2 - 5x + C$

(E) none of the above

---

20. If $y = e^{-x}\sin x$, then $\dfrac{d^2y}{dx^2} =$

(A) $-2e^{-x}\sin x$ (B) $-2e^{-x}\cos x$

(C) $-2e^{-x}(\sin x + \cos x)$ (D) $e^{-x}\sin x\cos x$

(E) $-2e^{-x}\sin x\cos x$

---

21. Find the area of the triangle formed by any line tangent to the curve $y = \dfrac{12}{x}$ in the first quadrant and the x- and y-axes.

---

22. The average value of the function $y = \sqrt{2x+1}$ from $x = 4$ to $x = 12$ is

(A) $\dfrac{49}{24}$ (B) $\dfrac{49}{12}$ (C) $\dfrac{97}{23}$ (D) $\dfrac{97}{12}$ (E) $\dfrac{49}{6}$

23.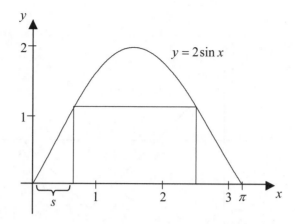

Find the area (to the nearest thousandth) of the largest rectangle that can be inscribed in one arch of $y = 2\sin x$. (Hint: let s be the distance from the origin to the beginning of the base of the rectangle.)

24. In $y = ax + b$ and the points (3, 15) and (4, 30) are on the graph. Find the rate of change of y with respect to x when $x = 5$.

25. $\displaystyle\int_0^\pi \sin(\pi x)\,dx =$

(A) $-\dfrac{2}{\pi}$ (B) $\dfrac{2}{\pi}$ (C) 2π

(D) $\dfrac{\cos(\pi^2)}{\pi}$ (E) $\dfrac{1-\cos(\pi^2)}{\pi}$

26.

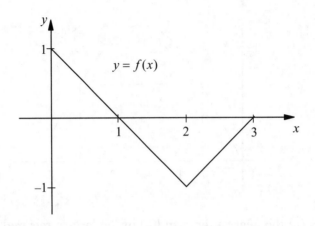

If $f(x)$ is the function shown above, then $\int_0^a f(x)\,dx$, $a \geq 0$, will equal 0 when

(A) $a = 0$ and $a = 2$ (B) $a = 1$ and $a = 3$
(C) $a = 0$ and $a = 3$ (D) $a = 1$ and $a = 4$ (E) $a = 3$ only

27.   If $y = \dfrac{\ln x}{\sin x}$, then $\dfrac{dy}{dx} =$

(A) $\dfrac{\cos x - \sin x \ln x}{\sin^2 x}$

(B) $\dfrac{\sin x - x \cos x \ln x}{x \sin^2 x}$

(C) $\dfrac{x \sin x - \cos x \ln x}{x \sin^2 x}$

(D) $\dfrac{\cos x - x \sin x \ln x}{x \cos^2 x}$

(E) $\dfrac{\sin x}{x} - \dfrac{\ln x}{\cos x}$

28. $\int_a^3 |x+1|\, dx$, where $a < -1$, is equal to

(A) $a - \dfrac{a^2}{2} + \dfrac{15}{2}$

(B) $a - \dfrac{a^2}{2} + \dfrac{17}{2}$

(C) $\dfrac{a^2}{2} - a + \dfrac{15}{2}$

(D) $\dfrac{a^2}{2} + a + \dfrac{17}{2}$

(E) none of the above

---

29. ▣ An airplane continues to climb after it reaches a cruising speed of 300 mph. If the angle at which the plane is climbing is $10°$, find the rate at which the plane is gaining altitude.

---

30. If $f(x) = x^2 \ln x$, then $f'(x) < 0$ for all

(A) $x < 0$

(B) $x > 0$

(C) $0 < x < \dfrac{1}{\sqrt{e}}$

(D) $0 < x < e$

(E) $0 < x < \sqrt{e}$

---

31. ■ A piece of steel at $1500°$ F is removed from the oven and placed in a room at $70°$ F. The temperature T of the steel, t minutes after it starts cooling, is given by $T = 70 + 1430e^{-0.2t}$. Find, to the nearest degree, the average temperature of the steel over the first hour.

32.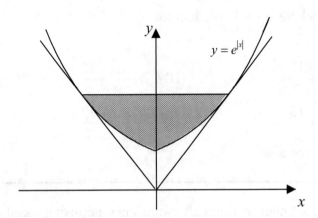

Two tangent lines can be drawn from the origin to the curve $y = e^{|x|}$. The area bounded by the line segment connecting the points of tangency and the curve $y = e^{|x|}$ (the shaded region) is revolved about the x-axis. Find the volume of the resulting solid.

2000

1. For what value of k is the function $y = \begin{cases} x+k \text{ , if } x < 2 \\ x^2 + 4 \text{ , if } x \geq 2 \end{cases}$ continuous at $x = 2$?

   (A) 2   (B) 4   (C) 6   (D) 8   (E) 10

---

2. How many points of inflection does the curve $y = (x-1)^{\frac{7}{3}}$ have?

   (A) 0   (B) 1   (C) 2   (D) 3
   (E) more than 3

---

3. If $f(x) = 4x + \dfrac{4}{x} + \dfrac{x}{4}$, $f'(x) =$

   (A) $\dfrac{5x^2 - 4}{x}$ (B) $\dfrac{17x^2 - 16}{4x^2}$

   (C) $\dfrac{4x^2 + 4 + 4x}{x^2}$ (D) $\dfrac{5x^2 + 4}{2x}$

   (E) $\dfrac{4x^2 - 4x + 1}{4x^2}$

---

4. $\displaystyle\lim_{h \to 0} \dfrac{\sqrt{a^2 + h} - a}{h} =$

   (A) 0   (B) $\dfrac{1}{2a^2}$ (C) $\dfrac{1}{2a}$ (D) $\dfrac{1}{a}$ (E) ∞

---

5. ▣ The height of a ball thrown upwards from the top of a hill 20 feet high with an initial velocity of 90 ft/sec is given by $h = -16t^2 + 90t + 20$ ft (where t is measured in seconds). How high above ground is the ball at its highest point?

   (A) 22.813   (B) 24.051   (C) 75.125   (D) 146.563   (E) 153.261

---

6. ▤   A rectangle is inscribed into the region bounded by the graph of $f(x) = (x^2 - 1)^2$ and the x-axis, in such a way that one side of the rectangle lies on the x-axis and two vertices lie on the graph of $f(x)$. What is the maximum possible area of such a rectangle?

(A) 0.286   (B) 0.572   (C) 0.781   (D) 1.000   (E) 1.414

7. ■

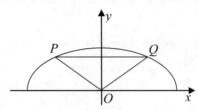

P and Q are two points on the ellipse $\dfrac{x^2}{a^2} + \dfrac{y^2}{b^2} = 1$, such that $\overline{PQ}$ is parallel to the x-axis. Find the coordinates of Q, in terms of a and b, when the area of $\triangle POQ$ is the largest.

8. ■

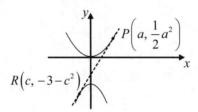

Point P in the first quadrant with coordinates $\left(a, \dfrac{1}{2}a^2\right)$ lies on the curve $y = \dfrac{1}{2}x^2$.

Point R in the third quadrant with coordinates $\left(c, -3 - c^2\right)$ lies on the curve $y = -3 - x^2$. Line PR is tangent to $y = \dfrac{1}{2}x^2$ at point P and is also tangent to $y = -3 - x^2$ at point R. Find a and c.

9. $\displaystyle\lim_{h\to 0}\frac{(2+h)^3+(2+h)-10}{h}=$

     (A)   9   (B)   10   (C)   11   (D)   12   (E)   13

10.   If $f(x)=2^x$, then $f(x+2)-f(x-2)=$

     (A) $\dfrac{17}{2^x}$ (B) $15\cdot 2^{x-2}$ (C) $17\cdot 2^{x-2}$ (D) $15\cdot 2^x$ (E) $17\cdot 2^x$

11.

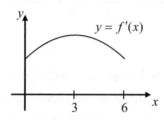

     The graph of $y=f'(x)$ is shown above. At what x does $f(x)$ reach its maximum on the interval $0\le x\le 6$?

12. ▪ Find the value of x at which the normal to the curve $y=x^2+1$ at $x=3$ intersects the curve again.

13.   If $3x+xy+4y=8$, the value of $\dfrac{d^2y}{dx^2}$ at the point (1, 1) is

     (A)   0   (B) $\dfrac{8}{25}$ (C) $\dfrac{8}{5}$ (D) $\dfrac{64}{25}$ (E) $\dfrac{64}{5}$

14.   The slope of the line tangent to the curve $y=f(x)$ is given by xy^2. If the curve passes through the point (2, 1), find the positive value of x when $y=-1$.

15. ▪ A car is traveling at 80 mph. When the driver hits the breaks, the car starts decelerating at a constant rate. It takes $\frac{1}{10}$ of a mile to stop. How many seconds does it take the car to stop from the point in time when the breaks are applied?

16. ▪

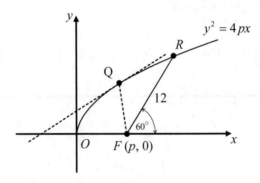

A comet moves in a parabolic orbit described by the equation $y^2 = 4px$, where p is the focal length constant. Sun is at the focal point, F with coordinates $(p, 0)$. At point R the comet is 12 million miles from the sun and makes an angle of $60°$ with the axis of the parabola. When the comet gets to point Q, the slope of $\overline{QF}$ is equal to the negative of the slope of the tangent line at Q. How far, in millions of miles, is Q from F?

17. If $\int_{-3}^{2} f(x)\,dx = 4$ and $\int_{-3}^{5} f(x)\,dx = -1$, then $\int_{2}^{5} f(x)\,dx =$

(A) −5   (B) −3   (C) 3   (D) 5
(E) cannot be determined

18. If $\lim\limits_{x \to -\infty} f(x) = 4$, $\lim\limits_{x \to \infty} f(x) = -6$, and $f'(x)$ is negative for all x, then

$\lim\limits_{x \to -\infty} f'(x) + \lim\limits_{x \to \infty} f'(x) =$

(A) −∞   (B) −2   (C) 0   (D) 10   (E) ∞

19. If $x = e^t$ and $y = t^2 - 3$, then $\dfrac{dy}{dx}$, evaluated at $t = 3$, is

   (A) $\dfrac{4}{e^3}$ (B) $\dfrac{6}{e^3}$ (C) $\dfrac{2}{e^2}$ (D) $\dfrac{6}{e^2}$

   (E) none of the above

20. The average value of the function $y = 4\cos 2x$ from $x = 0$ to $x = \dfrac{\pi}{4}$ is

   (A) $\dfrac{2}{\pi}$ (B) $\dfrac{4}{\pi}$ (C) $\dfrac{8}{\pi}$ (D) 2   (E) 4

21. The tangent and normal lines are drawn the curve $y = x^2 + 1$ at a point in the first quadrant where $x = a$. Find $\lim\limits_{a \to 0} k$, where k is the distance between the y-intercepts of these two lines.

22.

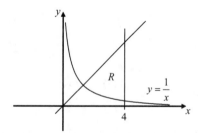

The region R, shown above, is bounded by $y = x$, $y = \dfrac{1}{x}$ and $x = 4$. If this region is rotated about the x-axis, the volume of the resulting solid is

   (A) $20\dfrac{1}{4}\pi$ (B) $21\dfrac{3}{4}\pi$ (C) $30\dfrac{1}{3}\pi$ (D) $40\dfrac{1}{2}\pi$ (E) $43\dfrac{1}{2}\pi$

23.■

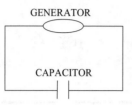

GENERATOR

CAPACITOR

In a circuit containing an alternating generator and a capacitor, the current $I(t)$, in amperes, is the derivative with respect to time of the charge on the capacitor $q(t)$, in coulombs. If $q(0) = 0$ and $I(t) = 5\sin\left(\dfrac{\pi}{20}t\right)$, find the maximum charge on the capacitor. Give your answer in terms of π.

24.■ The acceleration due to gravity is -32 ft/sec^2. An object is thrown downward. After falling $\dfrac{3}{4}$ of a foot it has doubled its initial velocity. What was the initial velocity?

25. $\displaystyle\int_1^4 \frac{e^{\sqrt{x}}}{\sqrt{x}}\,dx =$

(A) $2e(e-1)$ (B) $2e(e+1)$ (C) $5(e-1)$
(D) $3e^2 - e^3 + 7$ (E) $e^3 - 2e^2 + 4$

26.   Two tangent lines can be drawn from the origin to the curve $y = e^{|x|}$. Find the area of the triangle formed by these lines and the line segment connecting the points of tangency.

27.   If $f(x) = \displaystyle\int_{-10}^{x^2} \sqrt{1+t^2}\,dt$, then $f'(2) =$

(A) -10 (B) $\sqrt{5}$ (C) $2\sqrt{5}$ (D) $\sqrt{17}$ (E) $4\sqrt{17}$

28.

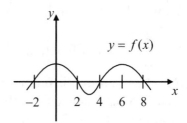

The graph of $y = f(x)$ is shown above. Over what interval(s) is the derivative of $f(x)$ increasing?

(A) $-2 \le x \le 0$ and $4 \le x \le 6$
(B) $2 \le x \le 4$
(C) $0 \le x \le 3$ and $6 \le x \le 8$
(D) $-2 \le x \le 2$ and $4 \le x \le 8$
(E) $-2 \le x \le 8$

29.   The region bounded by the function $y = |x+1| + |x-1|$ and the lines $x = -2$, $x = 2$, and the x-axis is rotated about the x-axis. Find the volume of the solid formed by the rotation.

30.   The root mean square value of a function $y = f(x)$ over the closed interval $[a, b]$ is

defined as $\sqrt{\dfrac{\int_a^b (f(x))^2 \, dx}{b-a}}$. How much larger is the root mean square value of

$f(x) = \sqrt{x}$ from $x = 1$ to $x = 49$ than the average value of this function on the same interval?

(A) $\dfrac{1}{8}$ (B) $\dfrac{1}{4}$ (C) $\dfrac{1}{3}$ (D) $\dfrac{1}{2}$ (E) $\dfrac{2}{3}$

31.■ A particle is moving in a straight line with an acceleration $a = \dfrac{dv}{dt} = -v^2$. At $t = 0$, $v = 1$. The distance covered from $t = 1$ to $t = 5$ is

(A) e^2 (B) $\ln 2$ (C) $\ln 3$ (D) $\ln 4$ (E) $\ln 12$

32.■ If an object is propelled upward with an initial velocity of v_0, then its velocity v is given by $v = \sqrt{v_0^2 - 2gR + \dfrac{2gR^2}{s}}$. v is a function of s, the distance from the center of the Earth; g and R are constants. From this relationship it follows that the object's acceleration times the square of its distance from the center is equal to a constant: $as^2 = k$. Find k in terms of g and R.

1999

1.

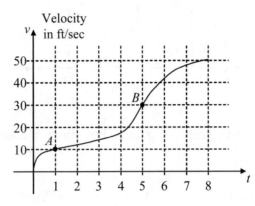

Velocity in ft/sec

Time in seconds

What is the average acceleration from A to B? (Give the answer in correct units.)

---

2.   If $y = f(x)^{g(x)}$ and $\lim_{x \to \infty}(\ln y) = 2$, then $\lim_{x \to \infty} f(x)^{g(x)} =$

(A) $\ln 2$ (B)   2   (C) e^2 (D) $2^{\ln 2}$
(E)   cannot be determined

---

3. ▣   Find the range of the function $f(x) = \dfrac{3x-2}{\sqrt{2x^2+1}}$. (Express your answer correct to 3

decimal places.)

---

4.   If $f(x) = \begin{cases} 3x^2+5 \text{ , if } x<1 \\ x^3+2x+5 \text{ , if } 1 \le x \le 4, \\ x+c \text{ , if } x>4 \end{cases}$ for what value of c is $f(x)$ continuous at

$x = 4$?

5.

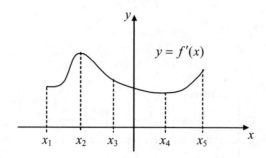

The figure above shows a graph of $f'(x)$. For which x-coordinate does $f(x)$ have the greatest value?

(A) x_1 (B) x_2 (C) x_3 (D) x_4 (E) x_5

6.   The curve $y = x^5 + 10x^4 - 5$ has points of inflection at $x =$

(A) 0 and -8 (B) 0 and -6 (C) -8 only
(D) -6 only   (E) 0 only

7.■

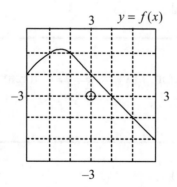

Given the graph of $f(x)$ above, sketch a graph of $f(f(x))$.

8.■   Determine the coefficients a, b, c, and d such that the curve
$f(x) = ax^3 + bx^2 + cx + d$ has a relative minimum at $(1, 5)$ and a point of inflection at $(-1, 21)$.

9.   If $\lim\limits_{h \to 0} \dfrac{f(x+h) - f(x)}{h} = g(x)$, then

(A) $f(x) = g(x)$ (B) $f'(x) = g(x)$
(C) $f(x) = g'(x)$ (D) $f'(x) = g'(x)$

(E) $\lim\limits_{h \to 0} \dfrac{g(x+h) - g(x)}{h} = f(x)$

10.

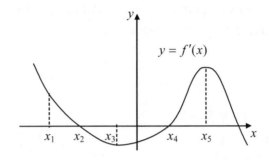

The figure above shows a graph of $f'(x)$. At the point $(x_1, f(x_1))$, the curve $y = f(x)$ is

(A)   rising and concave up
(B)   rising and concave down
(C)   falling and concave up
(D)   falling and concave down
(E)   neither rising nor falling

11.   Find the area bounded by the curves $y = 2 + |x - 1|$ and $y = -\dfrac{1}{5}x + 7$.

12. ▪ The value of the function $y = e^x - 2$ where it intersects $y = \sin x$ is

(A)   0   (B)   0.869   (C)   1   (D)   1.054
(E)   impossible to determine

13.

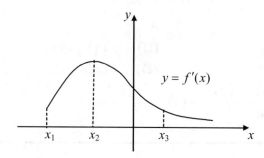

The figure above shows a graph of $f'(x)$. An equation for the line tangent to the curve $y = f(x)$ at the point of inflection is

(A) $y = f(x_2)$

(B) $y = f(x_3)$

(C) $y = f(x_1) + f'(x_1)(x - x_1)$

(D) $y = f(x_2) + f'(x_2)(x - x_2)$

(E) $y = f(x_3) + f'(x_3)(x - x_3)$

---

14.   The area enclosed by the graph of $y = x^2$ and the graph of its inverse function is

(A) $\dfrac{1}{6}$ (B) $\dfrac{1}{4}$ (C) $\dfrac{1}{3}$ (D) $\dfrac{1}{2}$ (E) $\dfrac{2}{3}$

15.■   The net acceleration of a miniature rocket shot from the ground is $a = 16 - 3t^2$ ft/sec^2. At the end of two seconds, the rocket's engine is turned off and the rocket is now affected by the acceleration due to gravity $a = -32$ ft/sec^2. How many feet above the ground does the rocket rise?

16.■ The rate of return on an investment is equal to the amount of annual income made on the investment divided by the amount invested (total cost and expenses): $R = \dfrac{\text{annual income}}{\text{amount invested}}$. The cost of erecting an office building is \$100,000 for the first floor, \$105,000 for the second, \$110,000 for the third, and so on. The total cost in dollars, $C = 100000n + \dfrac{5000n(n-1)}{2}$, where n is the number of floors. There are additional one-time expenses of \$360,000. If the net annual income for each floor is \$10,000, how many floors should be built in order to maximize the rate of return on the investment?

17. The slope of the line normal to the curve $y = xe^x$ at $x = -1$ is

(A) 0   (B) $\dfrac{2}{e}$ (C) $-\dfrac{e}{2}$ (D) e (E) undefined

18. If $f'(x) = 5x$, then the relationship between x and y would be described graphically by

(A) a parabola   (B) a circle   (C) an ellipse
(D) a hyperbola   (E) a straight line

19.▣

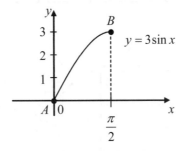

The x-coordinate of the point on the curve $y = 3\sin x$, between points A and B, where the tangent to the curve is parallel to the secant line joining points A and B is approximately

(A) 0.591   (B) 0.623   (C) 0.750   (D) 0.796   (E) 0.881

20. ▣ If $f(x) = x^\pi$ and $g(x) = \pi^x$, then $g'(4) - f'(4) \approx$

(A) 29.864   (B) 37.761   (C) 44.555   (D) 50.340   (E) 58.872

21.

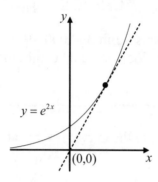

An equation for line L that is tangent to the curve $y = e^{2x}$ and passes through the origin is

(A) $y = 2e^{2x}$ (B) $y = ex$ (C) $y = 2x$ (D) $y = 2ex$ (E) $y = \dfrac{1}{2}x$

22. If $f(x) = \dfrac{e^{\sqrt{x}}}{2\sqrt{x}}$, what is the average value of $f(x)$ from $x = 1$ to $x = 4$?

23. ■

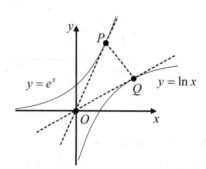

Tangent lines are drawn from the origin O to the point P on $y = e^x$ and point Q on $y = \ln x$. Find the area of $\triangle POQ$.

24. ■ Galileo was the first to determine the law for a freely falling body. He eventually came to the assumption that the velocity of a falling object is proportional to time: $v = \dfrac{ds}{dt} = kt$. This gives the equation $s = \dfrac{k}{2}t^2 + c$. If two measures of t and s are known, then the constants k and c can be found. For example, knowing $s = 16$ at $t = 1$ and $s = 64$ at $t = 2$, we can find $k = 32$. However, Galileo first conjectured that the velocity is proportional to the distance the object falls: $v = ks$. Using $t = 1, s = 16$ and $t = 2, s = 64$ determine the equation relating s and t and the value of s when $t = 0$.

25. If $f'(x) = e^x$, then the relationship between x and y could be described graphically by

   (A) an exponential curve
   (B) a log curve
   (C) a sine curve
   (D) a parabola
   (E) a straight line

26. If $y = \cos x$, then the derivative of y with respect to $\sin x$ is

   (A) $\sin^2 x$ (B) $-\sin x \cos x$ (C) $-\tan x$
   (D) $\sec x$ (E) $-\cot x$

27. The curve $y = x^3$ intersects the line $y = 7x - 6$ at three points, $(-3, -27)$, $(1, 1)$, and $(2, 8)$. Find the total area of the region bounded by $y = x^3$ and $y = 7x - 6$.

28. $F(x) = \displaystyle\int_1^{x^2} \dfrac{1+t}{\sqrt[5]{t^3}}\, dt$. $F'(32) =$

   (A) $\dfrac{33}{8}$ (B) $\dfrac{156}{8}$ (C) $\dfrac{1025}{64}$ (D) 528 (E) 1025

29.

The area of rectangle *RSTU* is equal to the area bounded by the curve $y = x^3$, the *x*-axis, and the lines $x = 1$ and $x = 3$. Find the *x*-coordinate of the point where the line segment $\overline{RS}$ intersects the curve $y = x^3$ between $x = 1$ and $x = 3$.

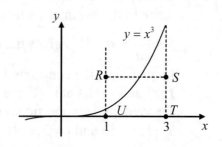

30.

The line $\overline{SQ}$ is tangent to the curve $y = \ln x$ at the point *Q*. $\overline{QR}$ is perpendicular to the *y*-axis. Find the length of $\overline{RS}$.

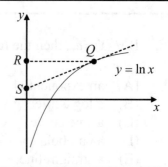

31. ■

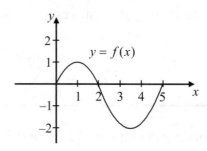

$g(x) = \int_0^x f(t)\,dt$, where *f* is the function whose graph is shown above. $g(5)$ is approximately

(A) −4.9   (B) −2.3   (C) 0   (D) 3.2   (E) 4.2

32. ■ A car traveling at a constant rate of 40 meters/second passes a stopped police cruiser that immediately pursues the car. The police cruiser accelerates at 4 meters/sec² until it reaches a speed of 48 meters/sec. It then continues at this speed until it catches the car. How many seconds does it take the police cruiser to catch the car?

1998

1. $\lim\limits_{x \to 10} \dfrac{4x^2 - 6x + 10}{50 + 4x^2} =$

   (A) -1 (B) 0 (C) $\dfrac{7}{9}$ (D) 1 (E) ∞

---

2. If $y = f(x)$ is an odd function, then $f'(x)$ is always a(n) _____ function.

   (A) even   (B) odd   (C) log   (D) trig   (E) irrational

---

3. If $y = f(x)$, $f(1) = 6$, and $f'(1) = 2$, then the equation of the line tangent to the curve at $x = 1$ is

   (A) $y = 6x - 4$ (B) $y = 6x - 8$ (C) $y = 2x + 8$

   (D) $y = 2x + 4$ (E) $y = -\dfrac{1}{2}x + 7$

---

4. ▣ If $f(x) = \sqrt[3]{3x^2 - 3x}$, then $f'(3)$ is approximately

   (A) 0.657 (B) 0.728 (C) 0.891 (D) 1.812 (E) 4

5.

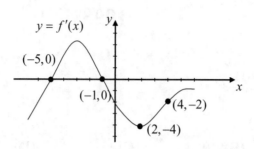

A graph of $y = f'(x)$ is shown above. The curve $y = f(x)$ has a relative maximum at $x =$

(A) −5   (B) −3   (C) −1   (D) 2   (E) 4

6.   If $y = f(x)$ is defined for all real numbers and is differentiable, then $f'(x)$

(A)   is defined for all real numbers
(B)   always has at least one relative maximum and one relative minimum
(C)   is always positive
(D)   must equal 0 when $f(x) = 0$
(E)   is concave down when $f(x)$ is negative

7.■

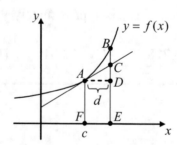

If $AD = d$, length of which line segment is equal to $f'(x) \cdot d$?

(A) $\overline{BC}$ (B) · $\overline{CD}$ (C) $\overline{BD}$ (D) $\overline{BE}$ (E) $\overline{AF}$

8.■   If $y\sqrt{x} = 8$ and $z = \dfrac{1}{2}x^2 + y^2$, find the minimum value of z.

9. $\lim\limits_{x \to \infty} \dfrac{x^2-1}{1-2x^2} =$

   (A) -1 (B) $-\dfrac{1}{2}$ (C) $\dfrac{1}{2}$ (D) 1

   (E) non-existent

10. ▪ The maximum value for the function $y = x^3 + x^2$ for $x < 0$ is approximately

    (A) -2.082 (B) 0   (C) 0.148   (D) 0.667   (E) 1.414

11. The area in the first quadrant bounded by $y = 4 - x^2$ is

    (A) $\dfrac{8}{3}$ (B) $\dfrac{16}{3}$ (C) $\dfrac{20}{3}$ (D) $\dfrac{28}{3}$ (E) $\dfrac{32}{3}$

12. The line normal to the curve $y = x^2$ at (2, 4) also intersects the curve at $x =$

    (A) -3 (B) $-\dfrac{5}{2}$ (C) $-\dfrac{9}{4}$ (D) -2 (E) $-\dfrac{3}{2}$

13.

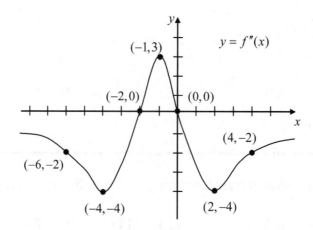

A graph of $y = f''(x)$ is shown above. For what values of x is the curve $y = f(x)$ concave up?

(A) $-2 < x < 0$
(B) $0 < x < 4$
(C) $-6 < x < -4$ and $2 < x < 4$
(D) $-6 < x < -2$ and $0 < x < 4$
(E) $x < -4$ and $x > 2$

14.   Find the maximum area of an isosceles triangle whose legs are each k inches long. (Your answer should be in terms of k.)

15.■ There are two lines that pass through the origin and are tangent to the curve $4x^2 + y^2 - 20x + 5 = 0$. Find the equations of both lines.

16.■

In the figure, PQ is a vertical line $x = c$. The line PR is tangent to the graph of $y = \dfrac{1}{x}$ at P and the line QS is tangent to the graph of $y = -\dfrac{1}{x^2}$ at Q. Find the limit of the area of the trapezoid PQSR as $c \to \infty$.

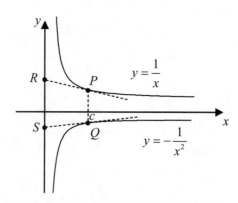

17. $\int \frac{\ln^2 x}{x} dx =$

(A) $\frac{1}{3}\ln^3 x + C$
(B) $\frac{1}{x^2} + \ln^2 x + C$
(C) $3\ln^3 x + C$

(D) $2\ln x - \frac{1}{x^2} + C$
(E) $-x\ln x + C$

18. Find the values of $\cos x$ for $0 < x < \frac{\pi}{2}$ where $y = \csc x$ intersects $y = \tan x$.

19. $\displaystyle\lim_{x \to 10^9} \tan\left(\frac{4x\pi - \pi}{4}\right) =$

(A) -1
(B) 0
(C) 1
(D) $\sqrt{3}$
(E) ∞

20. If $f'(x) = -\frac{x}{y}$, then the relationship between x and y could be described graphically by

(A) a parabola
(B) a circle
(C) an ellipse
(D) a hyperbola
(E) a straight line

21. ▪ The area bounded by the curve $y = \frac{1}{2} + \sin x$ and the x-axis from $x = 0$ to $x = 2\pi$ exceeds the area bounded by $y = \sin x$ and the x-axis from $x = 0$ to $x = 2\pi$ by approximately

(A) 0.511
(B) 2.142
(C) 2.511
(D) 3.142
(E) 4.511

22. ▪ The average value of the function $y = e^x$ on the interval from $x = -2$ to $x = 2$ is

(A) 1.637
(B) 1.813
(C) 1.881
(D) 1.924
(E) 2.114

23. ■ A line is tangent to the curve $y = f(x)$ at the point (x_1, y_1) and crosses the x-axis at $(x_2, 0)$. $f'(x_1) = m_1$. Express the distance between these two points in terms of y_1 and m_1.

24. ■ The function $f(x)$ is given by $f(x) = \dfrac{1}{\alpha\sqrt{2\pi}} e^{-\frac{x^2}{2\alpha^2}}$, where α is a positive constant.

Find the distance between the x-coordinates of the two inflection points of this function in terms of α.

25. If $\displaystyle\int_a^b f(x)\,dx = 6$ and $\displaystyle\int_a^b g(x)\,dx = -6$, which of the following must be true?

(A) $\displaystyle\int_a^b \frac{f(x)}{g(x)}\,dx = -1$

(B) $f(x) > g(x)$ for $a \le x \le b$

(C) $\displaystyle\int_a^b [f(x) - g(x)]\,dx = 0$

(D) $\displaystyle\int_a^b [f(x) + g(x)]\,dx = 0$

(E) $\displaystyle\int_a^b [f(x)g(x)]\,dx = -36$

26. $\displaystyle\int \frac{\sqrt[3]{x^2} - \sqrt{x}}{\sqrt[3]{x}}\,dx =$

(A) $\dfrac{2}{3}x^{\frac{3}{2}} - \dfrac{4}{3}x^{\frac{3}{4}} + C$ (B) $\dfrac{2}{3}x^{\frac{3}{2}} + \dfrac{4}{3}x^{\frac{3}{4}} + C$

(C) $\dfrac{3}{4}x^{\frac{4}{3}} - \dfrac{5}{6}x^{\frac{6}{5}} + C$ (D) $\dfrac{3}{4}x^{\frac{4}{3}} + \dfrac{5}{6}x^{\frac{6}{5}} + C$

(E) $\dfrac{3}{4}x^{\frac{4}{3}} - \dfrac{6}{7}x^{\frac{7}{6}} + C$

27. $\int_0^2 \sqrt{x}(3+x)\,dx \approx$

    (A) 6.79   (B) 7.92   (C) 8.12   (D) 8.32   (E) 8.52

28. If the slope of the line tangent to a curve is $\dfrac{x}{y}$ for all points of the curve, then which of the following is a possible choice for the curve?

    (A) $y = e^x$ (B) $y = x \ln x$

    (C) $x^2 - y^2 = 10$ (D) $x^2 + y^2 = 25$

    (E) $y = \dfrac{e^x}{x}$

29. If the area bounded by the curves $xy = 9$ and $x + y = 10$ is revolved about the x-axis, the volume of the generated solid is equal to

    (A) $\pi \int_1^9 \left(10 - x - \dfrac{9}{x}\right)^2 dx$

    (B) $\pi \int_1^9 \left[(10 - x)^2 - \left(\dfrac{9}{x}\right)^2\right] dx$

    (C) $\pi \int_1^9 \left[(10 - y)^2 - \left(\dfrac{9}{y}\right)^2\right] dy$

    (D) $\pi \int_1^9 \left(10 - y - \dfrac{9}{y}\right)^2 dy$

    (E) none of the above

30. If $x(t)$ is positive and increasing, then how many times larger is the rate of increase of x^2 than the rate of increase of x at $x = 5$?

    (A) 5   (B) 10   (C) 20   (D) 25   (E) 125

31. ■▪

Oil is leaking from a ruptured tanker at the rate of $500e^{-0.4t}$ gallons/hour. What is the average rate of leakage of oil in the first six hours, starting at $t = 0$? Give your answer correct to three places after the decimal point and in correct units.

32. ■

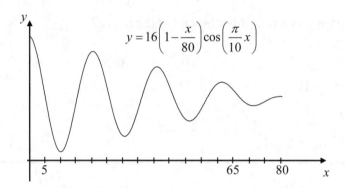

$$y = 16\left(1 - \frac{x}{80}\right)\cos\left(\frac{\pi}{10}x\right)$$

A roller coaster is in the shape of the curve $y = 16\left(1 - \dfrac{x}{80}\right)\cos\left(\dfrac{\pi}{10}x\right)$; x and y are in yards; $0 \le x \le 80$. A car moves with a horizontal velocity $\dfrac{dx}{dt} = 4$ yards/sec, which it maintains for the entire ride. How many times faster is the car moving vertically $\left(\dfrac{dy}{dt}\right)$ at $x = 5$ (on the first drop) than at $x = 65$ (on the last drop)?

1997

1. $\lim\limits_{x \to \infty} \dfrac{6\sqrt[3]{x} + 3\sqrt[6]{x} + 4}{\sqrt[3]{8x} - \sqrt[6]{x} - 10} =$

(A) $-\dfrac{2}{5}$ (B) 3   (C) $-\dfrac{13}{10}$ (D) 0   (E) ∞

---

2. For a given linear function $f(x)$, $\dfrac{f(b) - f(a)}{f(d) - f(c)} =$

(A) $\dfrac{b-a}{d-c}$ (B) $\dfrac{d-c}{a-b}$

(C) $\dfrac{f(d) - f(c)}{f(b) - f(a)}$ (D) $\dfrac{f(d) - f(c)}{f(a) - f(b)}$

(E) none of the above

3.

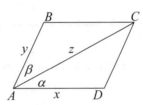

In parallelogram $ABCD$, $xz \sin \alpha =$

(A) $xy \sin(\alpha + \beta)$ (B) $2xy \sin(\alpha + \beta)$

(C) $\dfrac{1}{2} xy \sin(180 - (\alpha + \beta))$ (D) $\sqrt{x^2 + y^2 - 2xy \cos(\alpha + \beta)}$

(E) $yz \cos \beta$

---

4.   For what value of c is the function defined by $f(x) = \begin{cases} -x \text{ , if } x < -1 \\ -x^2 + x + c \text{ , if } -1 \le x \le 2 \\ 2x - 3 \text{ , if } x > 2 \end{cases}$

continuous at $x = -1$?

---

5.   The tangent line to the curve $y = 3x^4 - 10x + 3$ at $x = 1$ intersects the x-axis at the point

(A) $(-6, 0)$ (B) $(-4, 0)$ (C) $(0, -6)$ (D) $(3, 0)$ (E) $(4, 0)$

---

6.   If $f(x) = \sec\theta \csc\theta$ and $g(x) = \sec\theta \sin\theta$, then $f(x) - g(x) =$

(A) $\sin\theta$ (B) $\cos\theta$ (C) $\sec\theta$ (D) $\tan\theta$ (E) $\cot\theta$

7.■   Two tangent lines can be drawn to the curve $y = x^2 + x + 2$ from the point $(4, 13)$. The sum of the slopes of these two tangent lines is

(A) 12   (B) 14   (C) 16   (D) 18   (E) 20

8.■   The curve $y = ax + \dfrac{b}{x}$ has a relative maximum at the point $\left(-\sqrt{3}, -6\sqrt{3}\right)$. Find a and b.

9. If $f(x) = \sqrt{x-1}$ and $g(x) = x^2 + 13$, then the derivative of $f(g(x))$ at $x = 2$ is

   (A) $\dfrac{1}{8}$ (B) $\dfrac{1}{2}$ (C) 2   (D) 4   (E) 12

---

10. $\displaystyle\lim_{h \to 0} \dfrac{\sqrt[3]{64+h} + \sqrt{64+h} - 12}{h} =$

   (A) -12 (B) $-\dfrac{1}{12}$ (C) 0   (D) $\dfrac{1}{12}$ (E) 12

---

11. The equation of the line tangent to the curve $y^2 - 2x - 4y = 1$ at $(-2, 1)$ is

   (A) $y = -x - 1$ (B) $-y = -x - 3$
   (C) $3y = -x + 1$ (D) $5y = -x + 3$
   (E) none of the above

---

12. If $f(x) = \sqrt[3]{3x^2}$, then $f'(x) =$

   (A) $\dfrac{2}{\sqrt[3]{3x}}$ (B) $\dfrac{2x}{\sqrt[3]{3x^4}}$ (C) $\dfrac{2x}{\sqrt[3]{9x^4}}$ (D) $\dfrac{4x}{\sqrt[3]{3x^2}}$ (E) $\dfrac{4x}{\sqrt[3]{3x^4}}$

13. The point on the curve $y^2 = 4x$ closest to the point $(8, 0)$ is

(A) $\left(3, 2\sqrt{3}\right)$ (B) $\left(6, 2\sqrt{6}\right)$ (C) $\left(\dfrac{8}{3}, \dfrac{4}{3}\sqrt{3}\right)$

(D) $(9, 6)$ (E) $\left(10, 2\sqrt{10}\right)$

---

14. A car travels for 10 minutes. Its velocity is given by $v = 960t - 5t^3$, where t is in minutes and v is in ft/min. How many feet does the car travel from $t = 0$ to $t = 10$ minutes?

---

15. ▪ Find the area bounded by the curves $y^2 = 2x + 1$ and $y = x - 1$.

---

16. ▪

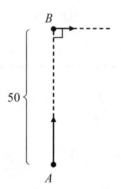

A particle at point A is 50 mm away from a second particle at point B. The first particle is moving towards point B at a constant rate and the second particle is moving at a right angle to the line AB at a rate that is $\dfrac{1}{3}$ of the rate of the first particle. The particles get closer to each other for $\dfrac{3}{4}$ of a second, and then begin to get further apart. How fast is the second particle moving in mm/sec?

17. Find $\int \dfrac{\sqrt[4]{x} + \sqrt{x}}{\sqrt[4]{x}}\, dx$.

18. If $f(x) = \dfrac{x^2}{e^x}$, then $f'(1) =$

(A) 0   (B) $\dfrac{1}{e}$ (C) $\dfrac{2}{e}$ (D) 2   (E) $2e$

19. If a particle traces the circle $x^2 + y^2 = 25$ and $\dfrac{dx}{dt} = -6$ when it reaches the point $(4, 3)$, what is the value of $\dfrac{dy}{dt}$ at that point?

20. One of the lines that can be drawn normal to the curve $x^2 - y^2 = 5$ and parallel to the line $2x + 3y = 10$ is

(A) $2x + 3y = 6$ (B) $2x + 3y = 8$
(C) $2x + 3y = 12$ (D) $2x + 3y = 14$
(E) $2x + 3y = 16$

21. If $f(x) = 3^{x^2}$, then $f'(x) =$

(A) 3^{x^2-1} (B) $2x3^{x^2}$
(C) $2x(\ln 3)3^{x^2}$ (D) $2(\ln 3x)x^2$
(E) $x^2 3^{x^2} \ln 3$

22. The derivative of $y = |\ln x|$ at $x = \dfrac{1}{2}$ is

(A) -2 (B) $-\dfrac{1}{2}$ (C) $\dfrac{1}{2}$ (D) 2
(E)   not defined

23.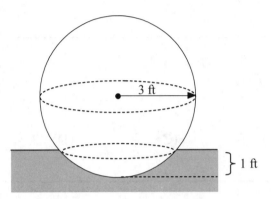

A sphere of radius 3 feet is put into the water and it sinks 1 foot into the water. By Archimedes principle, the weight of the water displaced by the sphere is equal to the weight of the sphere. Water weighs 62.4 pounds per cubic foot. What is the weight of the sphere? Give answer in terms of π.

24. Find the area of the region bounded by the curves $y = e^x$, $y = \ln x$, the line segment joining the points $(0, 1)$ and $(1, 0)$, and the line segment joining $(1, e)$ and $(e, 1)$.

25. $\int_0^1 x e^{x^2}\, dx =$

(A) $\dfrac{e-1}{2}$ (B) $\dfrac{e}{2}$ (C) $\dfrac{e+1}{2}$ (D) $\ln e^x$ (E) $\ln e^x - \ln x$

26.

A baseball diamond is a square with side 90 feet in length. A runner is moving from first base to second base at a constant speed of $8\sqrt{10}$ ft/sec. How fast is the runner moving away from home plate when he is 30 ft from first base?

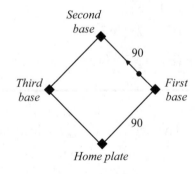

27. $\int_0^{\frac{\pi}{4}} \left(\tan^2 x + 1 \right) dx =$

(A) $1 - \dfrac{\pi}{2}$ (B) $\sqrt{2} - \dfrac{\pi}{2}$ (C) 1   (D) $1 + \dfrac{\pi}{2}$ (E) $\sqrt{2} + \dfrac{\pi}{2}$

28. $\int_{-1}^{4} \left| 2x - 4 \right| dx =$

(A) -5 (B) 5   (C) $\dfrac{19}{2}$ (D) 13   (E) $\dfrac{45}{2}$

29. $\dfrac{d}{dx} \int_0^x \dfrac{1}{1+t^4} dt =$

(A) $\dfrac{1}{1+x^4}$ (B) $\dfrac{4x^3}{1+x^4}$ (C) $\dfrac{1}{1+x^4} - 1$

(D) $\dfrac{1}{4x^3}$ (E) none of the above

30. An object is dropped with no initial velocity and an acceleration of 9.8 meters per second squared. A short while later the object is seen to cover a span of 24.5 meters in one second. What is the total time the object has fallen when it reaches the end of this 24.5 meter span?

31. ■

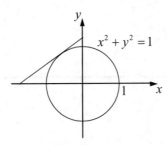

The circle $x^2 + y^2 = 1$ has a line segment drawn tangent to it in the second quadrant. The endpoints of the line segment are on the x- and y-axes. If the slope of this line segment is $\dfrac{3}{4}$, what is its length?

32. ■

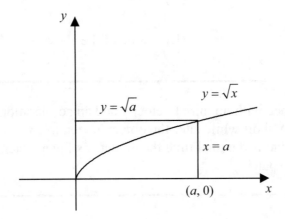

Let V_x be the volume obtained by revolving about the x-axis the region bounded by $y = \sqrt{x}$, $x = a$, and the x-axis. Let V_y be the volume obtained by revolving around the y-axis the region bounded by $y = \sqrt{x}$, $y = \sqrt{a}$, and the y-axis. Let $W = V_x - V_y$. Find the maximum value for W. Leave your answer in terms of π.

1996

1. $\lim\limits_{x \to 3} \dfrac{x^3 - 2x^2 - 3x}{x^3 - 9x} =$

    (A) 0   (B) $\dfrac{2}{3}$ (C) $\dfrac{3}{4}$ (D) 1   (E) ∞

---

2. If $f(x) = \sin\dfrac{x}{2}$ and $g(x) = \dfrac{3x^2 + 3x}{x+1}$, then $f\big(g(\pi)\big) =$

    (A) -1 (B) 0   (C) $\dfrac{1}{2}$ (D) $\dfrac{\sqrt{2}}{2}$ (E) 1

---

3. If $f(x) = |x+1|$, then $f'(-5) =$

    (A) -5 (B) -1 (C) 0   (D) 1   (E) 5

---

4. If $f(x) = \dfrac{1}{1-x}$, then $f^{(n)}(x)$ (the n-th derivative of $f(x)$) is

    (A) $\dfrac{n!}{(1-x)^{n+1}}$ (B) $\dfrac{(n+1)!}{(1-x)^n}$

    (C) $\dfrac{(-1)^n n!}{(1-x)^n}$ (D) $\dfrac{(-1)^{n+1} n!}{(1-x)^{n+1}}$

    (E) $\dfrac{(-1)^{n+1} n!}{(1-x)^n}$

5.

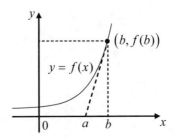

The point $(b, f(b))$, in the figure above, is a vertex of a rectangle opposite to the origin. The line from $(b, f(b))$ to $(a, 0)$ divides the rectangle into a trapezoid and a triangle. If the area of the trapezoid is twice the area of the triangle, then $a =$

(A) $\dfrac{1}{6}b$ (B) $\dfrac{1}{4}b$ (C) $\dfrac{1}{3}b$ (D) $\dfrac{1}{2}b$ (E) $\dfrac{2}{3}b$

---

6.   Let $C(x) = 8x^2 - 47x + 7200$ represent the total cost of producing a quantity x of some product. The marginal cost, $M = C'(x)$, is the derivative of the total cost function. The average cost, $A(x) = \dfrac{C(x)}{x}$. Find the difference between average cost and marginal cost at $x = 20$.

7.■   There are two lines which pass through the point $(4, 3)$ that have the sum of their x- and y-intercepts equal to -1. Find the equations of both lines.

8.■ $f(x) = \begin{cases} cx^2 + 5\text{, if } x < 1 \\ ax + b\text{, if } x \geq 1 \end{cases}$. The slope of the line tangent to the graph of $f(x)$ is -3 at $x = -1$. Find the values of a, b, and c such that $f'(x)$ is defined for all real numbers.

---

9.   If $5x^2 + 2xy - 3y^5 = 4$, then the value of $\dfrac{dy}{dx}$ at $(1, 1)$ is

(A) 0 (B) $\dfrac{4}{5}$ (C) $\dfrac{12}{13}$ (D) $\dfrac{14}{15}$ (E) 1

10.

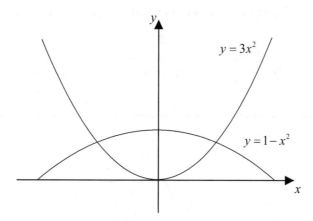

The four regions bounded by the curves $y = 3x^2$, $y = 1 - x^2$ and the two axes are all equal in area. The area of each of these regions is

(A) 1   (B) $\dfrac{2}{3}$ (C) $\dfrac{1}{2}$ (D) $\dfrac{1}{3}$ (E) $\dfrac{1}{6}$

11. The function $f(x) = x^{\frac{2}{3}} - 1$ does not satisfy Rolle's Theorem on the interval $[-1, 1]$ because

(A) $f(-1) \neq 0$
(B) $f(x)$ is not differentiable on $(1, -1)$
(C) $f(x)$ is not continuous on $\left[-1, 1\right]$
(D) $f(1) > f(-1)$
(E) $f(0) < 0$

12. A particle moves along the x-axis with acceleration given by $a = 12t - 6$. If $v = 3$ when $t = 0$, find the total distance the particle travels from $t = 0$ to $t = 2$.

13. The function $y = |x + 1| + |x| + |x - 1|$ can be expressed by 4 linear functions with domains for each. Give those 4 linear functions and their domains.

14. If $f(x) = \sqrt{2x+7}$, where $F'(x) = f(x)$ and $F(1) = 7$, then $F\left(-\dfrac{3}{2}\right) =$

(A) -2 (B) $-\dfrac{3}{2}$ (C) $-\dfrac{2}{3}$ (D) $\dfrac{2}{3}$ (E) $\dfrac{3}{2}$

---

15. ▪

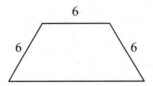

Find the maximum area of a trapezoid if three of the sides are each 6 units in length, as shown.

---

16. ▪

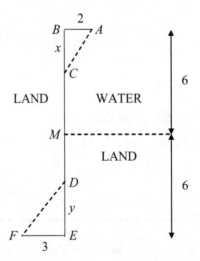

In a triathlon event, Janet must swim from point A (2 miles from B) to any point C on $\overline{BM}$, then bicycle to any point D on $\overline{ME}$ and finally run to point F (3 miles from E). $BM = ME = 6$ miles. Janet (with the aid of a strong current) can average 6 mph swimming, 10 mph cycling, and 8 mph running. Janet figured out point C so as to go from A to C to M in the shortest possible time. She also figured out point D to minimize the time from M to D to F. How far did she cycle from C to D?

17. If $f(x) = \sin x$ and the n-th derivative of $f(x)$ is equal to $f(x)$, then n can be equal to

(A) 1   (B) 2   (C) 3   (D) 4   (E) 5

18. The area bounded by $y = e^x$, $x = -1$, $x = 1$, and the x-axis is revolved about the x-axis. The volume thus generated is

(A) $\pi\left(e^2 - \dfrac{1}{e^2}\right)$

(B) $\dfrac{\pi}{2}\left(e^2 + \dfrac{1}{e^2}\right)$

(C) $\dfrac{\pi}{2}\left(e^2 - \dfrac{1}{e^2}\right)$

(D) $\pi\left(e^2 + \dfrac{1}{e^2}\right)$

(E) $\dfrac{\pi}{4}\left(e^2 + \dfrac{1}{e^2}\right)$

19. If $x = 3t - 6\ln t$, $y = \dfrac{4}{t}$, then the value of $\dfrac{dy}{dx}$ at the point $(12 - 6\ln 4,\ 1)$ is

(A) $-\dfrac{1}{2}$ (B) $-\dfrac{1}{3}$ (C) $-\dfrac{1}{6}$ (D) $\dfrac{1}{6}$ (E) $\dfrac{1}{3}$

20. The average value of the function $y = 3x^2$ over the interval $1 \le x \le 3$ is

(A) 2   (B) 12   (C) 13   (D) 24   (E) 26

21. In running 100 meters, Jesse can accelerate from a rest position at $8\dfrac{1}{3}$ m/sec^2 for 1.2 seconds. She can then maintain the velocity attained for the remainder of the race. How long will it take Jesse to run the 100 meters?

22.

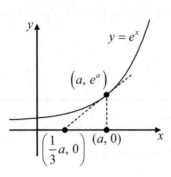

If the tangent line to the curve $y = e^x$ at $x = a$ intersects the x-axis at $x = \dfrac{1}{3}a$, then $a =$

(A) 1   (B) $\dfrac{3}{2}$ (C) 2   (D) $\dfrac{5}{2}$ (E) 3

23. ▪

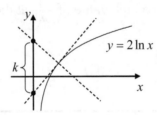

From any point on the curve $y = 2\ln x$, $x > 0$, the tangent and normal lines are drawn. These two lines intersect the y-axis at different points. Let k represents the length of the line segment joining these two y-intercepts. Find $\lim\limits_{x \to 0} k$.

24. ▪ A torpedo is ejected under water with an initial velocity of 100 m/sec. Its velocity at time t is given by $v = \dfrac{100}{1 + 0.25t}$ m/sec. (Its velocity is diminished by the resisting force of water such that $\dfrac{dv}{dt} = -0.0025v^2$ m/sec².) The torpedo must strike with a velocity of at least 50 m/sec to cause damage. What is the largest distance from which the torpedo could be ejected to cause damage?

25. If $f(x) = \sin 2x$, then $\dfrac{f'\left(\dfrac{\pi}{2}\right) - f'\left(\dfrac{\pi}{4}\right)}{f\left(\dfrac{\pi}{2}\right) - f\left(\dfrac{\pi}{4}\right)} =$

(A) -2 (B) -1 (C) 1 (D) 2
(E) not defined

---

26. The value of the slope of the line tangent to the curve $y = \dfrac{\tan x}{\sin x}$ at $x = \dfrac{\pi}{4}$ is

(A) $-\sqrt{2}$ (B) $-\dfrac{\sqrt{2}}{2}$ (C) $\dfrac{\sqrt{2}}{2}$ (D) 1 (E) $\sqrt{2}$

---

27. The value of c which satisfies Rolle's Theorem for the function $f(x) = \sin\left(x^2\right)$ on $\left[0, \sqrt{\pi}\right]$ is

(A) $\sqrt{\dfrac{\pi}{6}}$ (B) $\sqrt{\dfrac{\pi}{4}}$ (C) $\sqrt{\dfrac{\pi}{3}}$ (D) $\sqrt{\dfrac{\pi}{2}}$
(E) none of the above

---

28. If $f(x) = x \ln x,\ x > 0$, then $f'(x) < 0$ for all

(A) $x < 1$ (B) $x < e$ (C) $x < \dfrac{1}{e}$ (D) $x > \dfrac{1}{e}$ (E) $x > e$

---

29. Find the three largest positive values of x for which the function $y = \sin\dfrac{\pi}{x}$ has either a relative minimum or a relative maximum.

30.

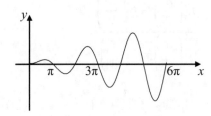

Find the total area of the region between the curve $y = x \sin x$ and the x-axis from $x = 0$ to $x = 6\pi$.

31. ■

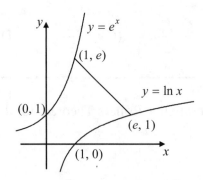

Find the area of the region bounded by the x- and y-axes, the curves $y = e^x$ and $y = \ln x$, and the line joining the points $(1, e)$ and $(e, 1)$. (Express your answer in simplest form in terms of e.)

32. ■ In a chemical reaction, the weight w of a substance varies with time t according to the equation $\ln \dfrac{w}{21 - w} = 10.5(t - 30)$, $w > 0$. Find the values of both w and t that maximize the rate of change $R = \dfrac{dw}{dt}$.

1995

1. If $f(x) = ax + b$, $f(3) = -2$, and $f(1) = -3$, then $b =$

   (A) $-\dfrac{7}{2}$ (B) $-\dfrac{5}{2}$ (C) $\dfrac{5}{2}$ (D) $\dfrac{7}{2}$ (E) $\dfrac{9}{2}$

---

2. If $x = \log_y x$, then when $x = \dfrac{1}{2}$, $y =$

   (A) $\dfrac{1}{4}$ (B) $\dfrac{1}{2}$ (C) 1 (D) 2 (E) 4

---

3. Consider the functions $y = x^2$ and $y = 2^x$. Which answer describes the functions best?

   (A) both are even
   (B) one is even, one is odd
   (C) both are odd
   (D) both are neither odd nor even
   (E) one is even, the other is neither odd nor even

---

4. $\displaystyle\lim_{h \to 0} \dfrac{3(-1+h)^2 - 2(-1+h) - 5}{h} =$

   (A) -8 (B) -4 (C) 0 (D) 4 (E) 8

---

5. If $f(x) = \left(\dfrac{x+1}{x-1}\right)^2$, then for $x \neq \pm 1$ $f(-x) =$

   (A) $f(x)$ (B) $-f(x)$ (C) $\dfrac{1}{f(x)}$ (D) $\dfrac{-1}{f(x)}$

   (E) none of the above

---

6. If $f(x) = (2x-3)^5$, then slope of the line tangent to the curve $y = f(x)$ at $x = 1$ is

   (A) -10 (B) -5 (C) 5 (D) 10 (E) 40

---

7. ■ On the number line, find two numbers such that the distance from each number to 7 is five times the distance from that number to -1.

---

8. ■ The function $y = 3x - x^3$ has one relative maximum and one relative minimum. The equation $|3x - x^3| = 2$ has four small integer solutions. For what values of x is $|3x - x^3| < 2$?

---

9. $\lim\limits_{x \to 1} \dfrac{x^3 - 1}{x^2 - 1} =$

   (A) 0 (B) 1 (C) $\dfrac{3}{2}$ (D) 3 (E) ∞

---

10. The area between the curve $y = 3 + 2x - x^2$ and the x-axis is

    (A) 1 (B) $5\dfrac{1}{3}$ C) $6\dfrac{1}{3}$ (D) $10\dfrac{2}{3}$ (E) $20\dfrac{2}{3}$

---

11. Given that $f'(x) = 3x^2 - 2$ and the graph of $y = f(x)$ contains the point $(-1, 5)$, find $f(x)$.

---

12. If $\lim\limits_{h \to 0} \dfrac{f(x+h) - f(x)}{h} = 4x$, then $\lim\limits_{h \to 0} \dfrac{f(x+h) - f(x-h)}{h} =$

    (A) $-4x$ (B) 0 (C) $2x$ (D) $4x$ (E) $8x$

13. ∎ With your calculator, find the positive value of x where the curve $y = 1 + \dfrac{1}{x}$ intersects the line $y = x$ (to the nearest thousandth).

---

14. If $xy + x^2 - y^2 = 1$, then the value of $\dfrac{d^2 y}{dx^2}$ at the point (1, 1) is

(A) −10   (B) −5   (C) 3   (D) 5   (E) 10

---

15. ∎ The Mean Value Theorem states that if $y = f(x)$ is continuous on the closed interval $[a, b]$ and differentiable on the open interval (a, b), then there exists at least one point c in (a, b) such that $f'(c) = \dfrac{f(b) - f(a)}{b - a}$. If

$$f(x) = \begin{cases} 2x - x^2, & \text{if } x < 1 \\ 2x^2 - 4x + 3, & \text{if } x \geq 1 \end{cases},$$ find two values of c in the interval $[a, b]$, where $a = 0$, $b = 2$, that satisfy the Mean Value Theorem.

---

16. ∎

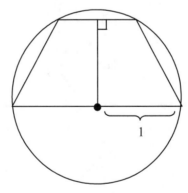

A trapezoid is inscribed in a circle of radius 1 where one base of the trapezoid is the diameter of the circle. Find the maximum area of the trapezoid.

---

17. The range of $y = 5^{\sin x} + 1$ is

(A) $y > 0$ (B) $-4 \leq y \leq 6$ (C) $-4 \leq y \leq 5$

(D) $\dfrac{6}{5} \leq y \leq 6$ (E) all real numbers

18. $\displaystyle\lim_{x\to\infty}\frac{e^x}{\ln\dfrac{1}{x}}=$

(A) $-\infty$ (B) 0   (C) 1   (D) e (E) ∞

19. $\displaystyle\int_1^2\frac{6x^2-4}{x}\,dx=$

(A) 0   (B) $9-\ln 16$ (C) $10\dfrac{2}{3}$ (D) $15-\ln 2$ (E) $20\dfrac{2}{3}$

20. The average value of the function $f(x)=3x^2-4$ from $x=2$ to $x=4$ is

(A) 6   (B) 12   (C) 18   (D) 24   (E) 48

21. If $f(x)=\dfrac{x-1}{x}$, then $f^{(n)}(x)$, the n-th derivative of $f(x)$, may be expressed as

(A) $\dfrac{n!}{x^{n+1}}$ (B) $\dfrac{(-1)^{n-1}n!}{x^{n+1}}$ (C) $\dfrac{(-1)^{n-1}n!}{x^n}$

(D) $\dfrac{(-1)^n n!}{x^n}$ (E) $\dfrac{(n+1)!}{x^{n+1}}$

22.

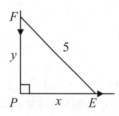

A 5 meter metal bar is being pulled at end E horizontally and to the right. The end at F is so attached that it slides vertically down toward P. If $x=t^2$, find $\dfrac{dy}{dt}$ when $t=\sqrt{3}$.

23.■ Find the volume of the solid generated by rotating the area bounded by $y = x^2$ and $x = y^2$ about the x-axis.

24.■ Evaluate $\int_0^{\frac{\pi}{3}} \left[\dfrac{\sec^2 x}{\csc x} \cdot \sin x \right] dx$.

25. Let $f(x) = \begin{cases} \dfrac{\sin x}{x}, & \text{if } x \neq 0 \\ c, & \text{if } x = 0 \end{cases}$. Find c such that $f(x)$ is a continuous function.

26. Find the coordinates of the point on the curve $y = e^x$ where the tangent line is parallel to the line $4x - y = 5$.

27. The curves $y = \sin x$ and $y = \cos x$ intersect twice on the interval $[0, 2\pi]$. The area of the region bounded by the two curves between the points of intersection is

(A) $\dfrac{\sqrt{2}}{2}$ (B) $\sqrt{2}$ (C) 2   (D) $2\sqrt{2}$ (E) 4

28. The x-coordinate of the inflection point of the curve $f(x) = e^{\tan^{-1} x}$ is

(A) -1 (B) $-\dfrac{1}{2}$ (C) 0   (D) $\dfrac{1}{2}$ (E) 1

29. If $\dfrac{dy}{dx} = x^2 y$ and $y = 1$ when $x = 2$, then for $y = e$, $x =$

(A) $-2e$ (B) $\ln 2$ (C) $\sqrt[3]{11}$ (D) 4
(E) none of the above

30. Assuming that the function $y = \log_x y$ ($x > 0$, $y > 0$) is differentiable, the slope of the tangent line to the curve at $y = \dfrac{1}{2}$ is

(A) 1

(B) $\dfrac{1}{1 + \ln 2}$

(C) $\dfrac{2}{1 + 2\ln 2}$

(D) $\dfrac{1}{1 - \ln 2}$

(E) $\dfrac{1}{\ln 2 - 1}$

31.■ The parametric equations for the function $y = f(x)$ are $y = t^2 + t$ and $x = 4t + 2$. If the slope of the tangent line at some point on the curve is m, then express the x- and y-coordinates of that point in terms of m in simplest form.

32.■ A car traveling at a rate of v ft/sec slows down in two stages. In the first stage, the deceleration rate is $-k$ ft/sec^2 until the velocity of the car becomes $\dfrac{1}{2}v$. In the second stage the deceleration rate is $-\dfrac{k}{2}$ ft/sec^2 until the car comes to a halt. The ratio of the time for the first stage to the time for the second stage is

(A) $1:4$ (B) $1:2$ (C) $2:3$ (D) $1:\sqrt{2}$ (E) $1:1$

1994

1. An even function has symmetry about

    (A) the x-axis   (B) the y-axis
    (C) the origin   (D) the line $y = x$
    (E) none of the above

---

2. Let $f(x) = \begin{cases} -2x+6, & \text{if } x < 2 \\ x^2-1, & \text{if } x \geq 2 \end{cases}$. The $\lim_{x \to 2} f(x)$ is

    (A) 3   (B) 2   (C) 10   (D) 5
    (E) non-existent

---

3. A car makes a trip in 10 minutes and its velocity is given by $v = 960t - 5t^3$, where t is in minutes and v is in ft/min. Find the maximum speed in ft/min during those 10 minutes.

---

4. The curve $y = 1 - 6x^2 - x^4$ has inflection points at $x =$

    (A) $\pm\sqrt{3}$ (B) 1   (C) -1 (D) ± 1 (E) none

---

5. It is desired to have the function $f(x) = \sqrt{\dfrac{16 - x^2}{4 - x}}$, $-4 \leq x < 4$ be made continuous over the interval $-4 \leq x \leq 4$. The value that must be assigned to $f(4)$ to accomplish this is

    (A) 0   (B) 2   (C) $2\sqrt{2}$ (D) 4   (E) $4\sqrt{2}$

---

6. Find the range of the function $y = \dfrac{1}{4}|x+2| - \dfrac{1}{4}|x-6|$ if the domain is all real numbers.

7.■   The line normal to the function $f(x) = 4 - x^2$ at $x = -1$ intersects the curve again. Find the value of the function at that point.

8.■   If $xy^2 = 16$ and $z = x^2 + y^2$, what is the minimum value of z?

---

9.   If $f(x) = \dfrac{1}{x}$, then, for some constant k, $f^{(n)}(x)$, the n-th derivative of $f(x)$, can be represented as

(A) $\dfrac{k}{x}$ (B) $\dfrac{k}{x^n}$ (C) $\dfrac{k}{x^{n-1}}$ (D) $\dfrac{k}{x^{n+1}}$ (E) $k \ln x$

---

10.   If $x^2 - 3xy - y = 5$, then the value of $\dfrac{dy}{dx}$ at $x = -1$ is

(A) -4 (B) -2 (C) 2 (D) 4
(E)   non-existent

---

11.   If $f(x) = \dfrac{x-1}{x+1}$, $x \neq -1$, then $\lim\limits_{h \to 0} \dfrac{f(1+h) - f(1)}{h} =$

(A) -1 (B) $-\dfrac{1}{2}$ (C) 0 (D) $\dfrac{1}{2}$ (E) 1

---

12.   The area in the first quadrant bounded by $y = \sqrt{4-x}$ is

(A) $\dfrac{4}{3}$ (B) $\dfrac{8}{3}$ (C) $\dfrac{16}{3}$ (D) $\dfrac{22}{3}$ (E) $\dfrac{32}{3}$

---

13.   Given $f(x) = \begin{cases} ax^2, & \text{if } x \leq 2 \\ bx - 6, & \text{if } x > 2 \end{cases}$, find the value of a that will make $f(x)$ differentiable at $x = 2$.

14. A point (x, y) moves so that its distance from the point $(0, 4)$ is always $\dfrac{4}{3}$ its distance from the line $4y = 9$. The locus of all these points is described by

(A) a circle   (B) a parabola   (C) an ellipse
(D) a hyperbola   (E) a straight line

15. ■ The side of a square, s, is increasing at a rate of k units per second. Find the rate at which the area of the square is increasing.

16. ■

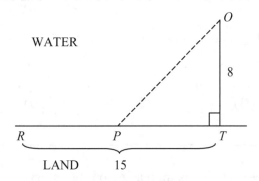

An oil well at O is in the ocean, 8 miles from T on a straight shoreline.
$RT = 15$ miles. The oil has to go from O to R. The cost of laying pipe per mile is $90,000$ underwater and $54,000$ on land. The cheapest method of placing the pipe is to lay $\overline{OP}$ underwater and $\overline{PR}$ on land, where P is some point on $\overline{RT}$. What is the amount of money that can be saved by using this method instead of going directly from O to R underwater?

17. $\displaystyle\lim_{x \to 0} \dfrac{1 - \cos x}{x^2} =$

(A) 1   (B) $\dfrac{1}{2}$ (C) 0   (D) −1   (E) ∞

18. The function $f(x) = \dfrac{2x-2}{\ln x}$ is defined for all $x > 0$ except $x = 1$. The value that must be assigned to $f(1)$ to make $f(x)$ continuous at $x = 1$ is

   (A) −2   (B) −1   (C) 0   (D) 1   (E) 2

19. $\displaystyle\int_0^1 \dfrac{e^x - 1}{e^x}\, dx =$

   (A) 0   (B) $\dfrac{1}{e}$ (C) 1   (D) e (E) $1 + e$

20. If $f(x) = e^x$ and $g(x) = \dfrac{1}{x}$, then the derivative of $f\big(g(x)\big)$, evaluated at $x = 2$, is

   (A) $-\dfrac{\sqrt{e}}{2}$ (B) $-\dfrac{\sqrt{e}}{4}$ (C) $-\dfrac{e}{4}$ (D) $\dfrac{e}{2}$ (E) $\sqrt{e}$

21. The function $f(x) = x - e^x$ is increasing on the interval

   (A) $x \le 0$ (B) $-1 \le x \le 0$ (C) $-1 \le x \le 1$
   (D) $0 \le x \le 1$ (E) $x \ge 0$

22. $\displaystyle\int_2^4 \sqrt{\left(x^2 - 4\right)^2}\, dx =$

   (A) −20   (B) 4   (C) $\dfrac{32}{3}$ (D) 20

   (E) does not exist

23. 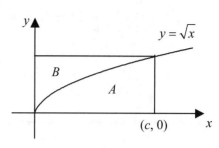 At some point $(c, 0)$ on the x-axis, a vertical line segment is drawn to a point on the curve $y = \sqrt{x}$, and from that point a horizontal line is drawn to the y-axis. These lines and the graph of $y = \sqrt{x}$ form two regions, A and B, as shown above. Region A is rotated about the x-axis and region B is rotated about the y-axis. Find the value of c for which the volumes of the two solids are equal.

24.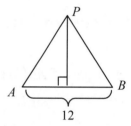

$AB = 12$ inches. An object P starts at the midpoint of $\overline{AB}$ and moves up at a constant rate of 2 in/sec, so that $\overline{PA}$ remains equal to $\overline{PB}$. What is the rate (in radians per second) at which $\angle APB$ is decreasing at the moment when $\triangle APB$ becomes equilateral?

25. If the domain of the function $y = \sin x$ is restricted to $\dfrac{\pi}{6} \le x \le \dfrac{5\pi}{6}$, then the range of the function is

(A) $-\dfrac{1}{2} \le y \le \dfrac{1}{2}$ (B) $-1 \le y \le 1$

(C) $0 \le y \le \dfrac{1}{2}$ (D) $0 \le y \le 1$

(E) $\dfrac{1}{2} \le y \le 1$

26. Express the derivative of $\tan x - x$ in terms of $\tan x$.

27. Which of the following does NOT satisfy the conditions for Rolle's Theorem?

(A) $f(x) = x^{\frac{2}{3}} - 1$ on $[-1, 1]$ (B) $f(x) = \sqrt{4 - x^2}$ on $[-2, 2]$
(C) $f(x) = \sin x$ on $[0, \pi]$ (D) $f(x) = x^4 - 1$ on $[-1, 1]$
(E) all of the above satisfy the conditions

28. If $f(x) = \dfrac{e^x}{e^x + 1}$, then the inverse function of f, $f^{-1}(x) =$

(A) $\dfrac{x}{1-x}$ (B) $\ln\left|\dfrac{x}{1-x}\right|$ (C) $\dfrac{1-x}{x}$ (D) $\ln\left|\dfrac{1-x}{x}\right|$ (E) $\ln\left|\dfrac{1+x}{x}\right|$

29. Find an expression for y in terms of x if $\dfrac{dy}{dx} = 6x\sqrt{3x^2 + 1}$ and $y = 1$ when $x = 0$.

30. If $x = ce^{-at}\cos(bt)$, where a, b, and c are constants, then $\dfrac{dx}{dt} =$

(A) $abce^{-at}\sin(bt)$ (B) $-ace^{-at}\cos(bt)$

(C) $-bce^{-at}\sin(bt)$ (D) $-ce^{-at}\left[\cos(bt) + \sin(bt)\right]$

(E) $-ce^{-at}\left[a\cos(bt) + b\sin(bt)\right]$

31. ■ A particle is moving clockwise on the ellipse $16x^2 + 9y^2 = 400$. What are the coordinates of particle's position in the first quadrant where the y-coordinate is decreasing at the same rate as the x-coordinate is increasing?

32. ■ The relative error of a variable x is defined as $\dfrac{dx}{x}$, where dx is the differential of x.

The length of a pendulum L and its period P are related by the formula $P = 2\pi\sqrt{\dfrac{L}{g}}$, where g is acceleration due to gravity. If the relative error in L is equal to $k\%$, then what is the relative error in P?

1993

1. $\lim\limits_{a \to b} \left(\dfrac{a^2 - b^2}{a - b} + 3ab \right)$ is

   (A) $3a^2$ (B) $5b$ (C) $2b + 3b^2$ (D) $3a^2 + a$
   (E) not defined

---

2. If the domain of the function $f(x) = 19 - 2x$ is restricted to $-3 \leq x \leq 5$, then the range of $f(x)$ is

   (A) $9 \leq y \leq 13$ (B) $9 \leq y \leq 25$
   (C) $13 \leq y \leq 21$ (D) $17 \leq y \leq 21$
   (E) $17 \leq y \leq 25$

---

3. If $f(x) = x^2 - x$, then $f(x+1) - f(x) =$

   (A) 2   (B) $2x$ (C) x (D) 1   (E) 0

---

4. The graph of $f(x) = \dfrac{x^2 - 5x + 6}{x^2 - 4}$ has vertical asymptotes at

   (A) $x = 0$ only   (B) $x = -2$ only
   (C) $x = 2$ only   (D) $x = 2$ and $x = -2$
   (E) $x = 3$ only

---

5. The slope of the line tangent to the curve $f(x) = x^3 + 3x^2 - 24x + 4$ at the point of inflection is

   (A) -27 (B) -15 (C) 30   (D) 32
   (E) none of the above

---

6.   The function $f(x) = \dfrac{3x^2 - 3x}{x^2 - 1}$ is not defined at $x = \pm 1$. What value should be assigned to $f(1)$ to make $f(x)$ continuous at that point?

7.■ What is the largest and what is the smallest slope for a tangent to the curve $y = 5x^3 - 15x^2 + 19x + 2$ in the interval $-2 \le x \le 3$?

8.■ Find the inflection point, or points, if any, on the graph of $f(x) = (x-3)^{\frac{1}{5}} - 4$.

9.   If $f(x) = \begin{cases} 4 & \text{, if } x < 0 \\ x^2 & \text{, if } 0 \le x \le 2, \\ -4 & \text{, if } x > 2 \end{cases}$ then the range of $f(x)$ is

(A) $[-4, 0] \cup \{4\}$ (B) $\{-4\} \cup [0, 4]$ (C) $[-4, 4]$

(D) $[0, \infty)$ (E) all real numbers

10. If $F'(x) = (3x+1)^{\frac{3}{2}}$ and $F(1) = 4$, then $F(x) =$

(A) $\dfrac{6\sqrt{3x+1}}{3}$ (B) $\dfrac{4\sqrt{3x+1}}{9}$

(C) $\dfrac{2(3x+1)^{\frac{5}{2}} - 4}{15}$ (D) $\dfrac{2(3x+1)^{\frac{5}{2}} - 44}{5}$

(E) $(3x+1)^{\frac{5}{2}} + 4$

11. If a particle is moving clockwise on the circle $x^2 + y^2 = 1$, at the instant when $\dfrac{dx}{dt} = 4$ and $\dfrac{dy}{dt}$ is positive the particle is in quadrant

(A) I   (B) II   (C) III   (D) IV   (E) I or II

12. Find the point on the curve $x = 4y - y^2$ where the tangent to the curve is a vertical line.

13. Find the point on the curve $y = x^2$ where the tangent to the curve is parallel to the secant line connecting $(-1, 1)$ and $(2, 4)$.

14. If $f(x) = \sqrt[3]{x}$, $a = 0$, $b = 8$, and $f(b) - f(a) = (b-a)f'(c)$, then the value of c is

(A) $\dfrac{4}{3}\sqrt{2}$ (B) $\dfrac{9}{8}\sqrt{2}$ (C) $\dfrac{8}{9}\sqrt{2}$ (D) $\dfrac{4}{3}\sqrt{3}$ (E) $\dfrac{8}{9}\sqrt{3}$

15. ■

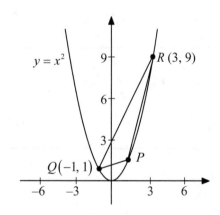

Archimedes, long ago, proved that if Q, R, and P are points on a parabola and if P is the point on the parabola between Q and R which is at maximum distance from $\overline{QR}$, then the area of $\triangle QPR = \dfrac{3}{4}$ of the area of the region enclosed between $\overline{QR}$ and the parabola. If the equation of the parabola is $y = x^2$, the coordinates of R are $(3, 9)$, the coordinates of Q are $(-1, 1)$, and P is at a maximum distance from $\overline{QR}$, then what is the area of $\triangle QPR$?

16.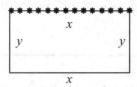

Mrs. Flynn wishes to design a rectangular flower garden with one side having an ornamental design. The fencing for three of the sides is $4 a foot and it is $5 a foot for the special side. If she wants the cost of the fencing to come to $1 for every square foot of the area of the garden, then what is the minimum cost for the fencing?

17. $\lim_{x \to \infty} xe^{-x} =$

(A) 0   (B) 1   (C) ∞   (D) π (E) e

18. The average value of the function $f(x) = 4x^3 - 2x$ over the interval $2 \le x \le 3$ is

(A) 30   (B) 37   (C) 60   (D) 74   (E) 90

19. $\int_1^2 \ln x \, dx =$

(A) $\ln 1$ (B) $\ln 2$ (C) $2\ln 2 - 1$ (D) $3\ln 2 - 1$
(E) none of the above

20. Find the area of the triangle formed by the x-axis and the tangent and normal lines to the curve $y^2 = 4x$ at the point (1, 2).

21. If $f(x) = \int_2^x \frac{1}{1+t^3} dt$, then the value of $f'(2)$ is

(A) $-\dfrac{7}{18}$ (B) 0   (C) $\dfrac{1}{9}$ (D) $\dfrac{1}{3}$
(E) none of the above

22. If $y = \left(e^{\frac{1}{x}} \right)^k$, k is a constant, then $y' =$

(A) $ke^{\frac{1}{x}}$ (B) $\dfrac{k}{x} e^{\frac{k-x}{x}}$ (C) $-\dfrac{k}{x^2} e^{\frac{k}{x}}$ (D) $-\dfrac{k}{x^{\frac{2}{k}}} e^{\frac{k}{x}}$

(E) none of the above

23. ▪ An object starts moving with zero initial velocity and constant acceleration. The distances the object moves in three equal consecutive time intervals are in the ratio of $1 : a : b$. Find the values of a and b.

24. ▪ If an object weighs 121 pounds at the surface of Earth then its weight when it is r miles above the surface of Earth is $w = 121 \left(1 + \dfrac{1}{4000} r \right)^{-2}$ lbs. If the object travels directly away from Earth and shortly after takeoff reaches a constant velocity of 11 miles/sec, then at what height in miles is the object's weight decreasing at $\dfrac{1}{2}$ lbs/sec?

25. Find $\displaystyle\lim_{x \to 2} \dfrac{\left(x^2 + 5 \right)^{\frac{1}{2}} - 3}{x - 2}$.

26. If $y = \ln \sqrt{x}$, then $y > 1$ when

(A) $x > 1$ (B) $x > e$ (C) $x > e^2$ (D) $x < e$ (E) for all x

27. For which of the following functions does $\dfrac{d^3 y}{dx^3} = \dfrac{dy}{dx}$?

I. $y = e^x$ II. $y = e^{-x}$ III. $y = \sin x$

(A) I only   (B) II only   (C) III only   (D) I and II   (E) I and III

28. For the curve $f(x) = x \ln x + (1-x) \ln(1-x)$ find the value of x in the interval $0 < x < 1$ where $f(x)$ has a minimum.

29. The volume generated by revolving about the x-axis the area enclosed by $y = \tan x$, $x = \dfrac{\pi}{3}$, and the x-axis is

(A) $\pi\left(1 - \dfrac{\pi}{3}\right)$

(B) $\pi\left(\sqrt{2} - \dfrac{\pi}{3}\right)$

(C) $\pi\left(\sqrt{3} - \dfrac{\pi}{3}\right)$

(D) π

(E) $\pi\sqrt{3}$

30. Which of the following curves passing through the point $(4, 1)$ satisfies the differential equation $y' = xy$?

(A) $y = e^{x-4}$

(B) $y = 2x - 7$

(C) $y = \sqrt{x^2 - 15}$

(D) $y = \sin^2 x + \cos^2 x$

(E) none of the above

31. ■ Find the volume of the solid formed by revolving about the y-axis the region bounded by $y = \dfrac{1}{x^2 + 4}$, the y-axis, and the line $y = \dfrac{1}{8}$.

32. ■ The probability that a radio transistor will fail after c months and before d months is given by the formula $p = k \displaystyle\int_c^d e^{-kt} \, dt$, where k is a constant. If the probability that the transistor will fail within the first year ($c = 0$, $d = 12$) is 20%, then what is the probability that it will fail during the second year? (Transistors can improve with age.)

1992

1. $\lim\limits_{x \to a} \dfrac{x^2 - a^2}{a - x} =$

    (A) $-2a$ (B) 0   (C) 1   (D) $2a$ (E) ∞

---

2. Find the range of the function $f(x) = \sqrt{6 - x - x^2}$.

---

3. B and 9 are solutions to the equation $x^2 - 4x = A$. Find the value of $A + B$.

---

4. Two tangent lines can be drawn to the curve $y = x^2 + 4x$ from $(0, -4)$. The slopes of those two tangent lines are

    (A) -5 and -1 (B) -2 and 2
    (C) 0 and 8   (D) 1 and 5
    (E) none of the above

---

5. The number of relative extrema on the graph of $y = x^3 - 3x^2 + 3x$ is

    (A) 0   (B) 1   (C) 2   (D) 3   (E) 4

6.

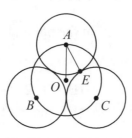

O is the center of the circle which passes through the centers of the three equal circles, A, B and C. The ratio of AO to AE is approximately

    (A) 1.047   (B) 1.061   (C) 1.155   (D) 1.214   (E) 1.299

7.■ Find the inflection point(s), if any, on the graph of $f(x) = (2x+3)^{\frac{3}{5}} - 4$.

8.■ Given $f(x) = \begin{cases} ax^2 + bx + 1, & \text{if } x < \dfrac{1}{2} \\ x^3 + 2, & \text{if } x \geq \dfrac{1}{2} \end{cases}$, find the values of a and b that will make

$f(x)$ differentiable at $x = \dfrac{1}{2}$.

9. The remainder when $4x^3 + kx^2 + 3x + 1$ is divided by $x - 1$ is 4. The value of k is

(A) −4   (B) −2   (C) 0   (D) 3
(E) none of the above

10. If $f(x) = x^4$, find the ratio of the slope of the tangent to the graph of $f''(x)$ at $x = 1$ to the slope of the tangent to the graph of $f(x)$ at $x = 1$.

11. Of the following, which two have equal value?

I. $\sqrt{\sqrt[3]{4 \cdot 2}}$ II. $\sqrt[3]{2\sqrt{4}}$ III. $\sqrt[3]{4\sqrt{2}}$ IV. $\sqrt{2\sqrt[3]{4}}$

(A) I and II   (B) I and III   (C) II and III
(D) II and IV   (E) III and IV

12. The tangent to the curve $y = x^3$ at the point $(1, 1)$ intersects the curve again at the point

(A) $(-3, -27)$ (B) $(-2, -8)$ (C) $(-1, -1)$
(D) $(0, 0)$ (E) none of the above

13.   If $\lim\limits_{h\to 0}\dfrac{f(x+h)-f(x)}{h}=3x^2+x$, then $\lim\limits_{h\to 0}\dfrac{f(x+h)-f(x-h)}{h}=$

(A) $-3x^2-x$ (B) $3x^2+x$ (C) $-6x^2-2x$

(D) $6x^2+2x$ (E)   none of the above

14.   There are two values for c which satisfy the Mean Value Theorem,
$f'(c)=\dfrac{f(b)-f(a)}{b-a}$, for the function $f(x)=(x-1)^3$ from $x=-1$ to $x=3$. Find
these values.

15.■

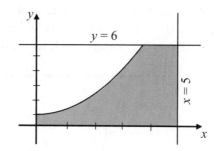

Find the area of the shaded region, shown in the figure above, bounded by the
parabola $16y=5x^2+16$ and the lines $y=0$, $x=0$, $y=6$, and $x=5$.

16.

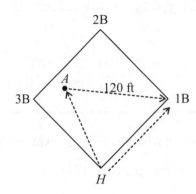

In a baseball game, the third baseman (*A*) fields a ball at a point 120 ft from first base. The ball has taken 1.40 sec to get to him and it takes him another second to release the ball at an average speed of 100 ft/sec to first base. The batter accelerates immediately, on hitting the ball, at a constant acceleration of 14.4 ft/sec^2 for the first 45 ft toward first base. He then maintains his velocity for the remaining 45 ft. The ball arrives to first base before the batter. By how many seconds?

17. Recall that $1+2+3+...+n = \dfrac{n(n+1)}{2}$. Find $\displaystyle\lim_{n\to\infty}\dfrac{1+2+3+...+n}{n^2+2n}$.

18. If $f(x)=\dfrac{\ln x}{1-\ln x}$, then $f'(1)=$

   (A) 0   (B) $\dfrac{1}{2}$ (C) 1   (D) 2   (E) ∞

19. If $f(x)=\dfrac{2x}{1-2x}$, then $f^{-1}(x)$ (the inverse of *f*) can be expressed as

   (A) $\dfrac{x}{1+2x}$ (B) $\dfrac{x}{2+2x}$ (C) $\dfrac{x}{1-2x}$ (D) $\dfrac{x}{2-2x}$
   (E)   none of the above

20. If $\log(10!)=a$, find $\log(9!)$ in terms of *a*.

21. Find the area bounded by the curves $y = x^2$ and $y = -|x| + 6$.

22. Given $y = 1 + xe^y$, express $\dfrac{dy}{dx}$ in terms of y only.

23. ■ Find the volume of the solid generated when the area bounded by $y = e^{-x}$, $x = 0$, $y = 0$, and $x = \ln 5$ is rotated about the x-axis.

24. ■

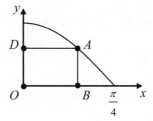

A rectangle $ABOD$ is inscribed into the region bounded by the x- and y-axis and the graph of $y = \cos 2x$, as shown above. What is the greatest perimeter that such rectangle can have?

25. $\displaystyle\lim_{x \to 1} \frac{\ln x}{x^2 - 1} =$

(A) 0   (B) $\dfrac{1}{2}$ (C) 1   (D) $\dfrac{3}{2}$ (E) ∞

26. Find the area bounded by the x-axis, the curve $y = |\sin x|$, and the lines $x = -\dfrac{\pi}{2}$ and $x = \dfrac{\pi}{2}$.

27. The average value of $y = \tan^2 x$ over the interval from $x = 0$ to $x = \dfrac{\pi}{4}$ is

(A) $\dfrac{4}{\pi} - 1$ (B) $\dfrac{\sqrt{3}}{\pi}$ (C) $\dfrac{2}{\pi}$ (D) $\dfrac{4}{\pi}$

(E) none of the above

28. $\log_2 10 \cdot \log_{10} 4 =$

(A) 1 (B) 2 (C) 4 (D) 5 (E) 20

29. Find the minimum value of $y = x^x$ over the interval $0 < x < 1$.

30. If $\dfrac{dy}{dx} = 2xy$ and $y = 1$ when $x = 1$, then $y(2) =$

(A) $\ln 2$ (B) $\ln 3$ (C) $e^2 - 1$ (D) e^2 (E) e^3

31.■ A particle moves along the x-axis so that its x-coordinate at any time t is given by $x = c \sin kt + d \cos kt$ $(k > 0)$. If the acceleration $a(t) = -3x$, find k.

32.■ Find the volume of a solid generated by revolving the region bounded by $y = \sin^{-1} x$, the x-axis, and $x = 1$ about the x-axis.

1991

1. $\displaystyle \lim_{x \to \frac{\pi}{4}} \frac{\csc^2 x - \tan^2 x}{\csc x - \tan x} =$

(A) 0   (B) $\sqrt{2} - 1$ (C) 1   (D) $\sqrt{2}$ (E) $\sqrt{2} + 1$

---

2. Find the natural domain of the function $y = \sqrt{5 - \sqrt{5 - x}}$.

---

3. By how much does the area of a square with side d exceed the area of a circle with diameter d?

(A) $d^2 \left(\dfrac{4 - \pi}{2} \right)$ (B) $d^2 \left(\dfrac{4 - \pi}{3} \right)$

(C) $d^2 \left(\dfrac{4 - \pi}{\pi} \right)$ (D) $d^2 \left(\dfrac{4 - \pi}{4} \right)$

(E) none of the above

---

4. The slope of the line tangent to the curve $f(x) = \dfrac{4}{15} x^{\frac{5}{2}} - \dfrac{16}{3} x^{\frac{3}{2}}$ at the point of inflection is

(A) $-\dfrac{32}{3}$ (B) $-\dfrac{8}{5}$ (C) $-\dfrac{16}{7}$ (D) $-\dfrac{4}{3}$ (E) $-\dfrac{8}{7}$

---

5. If $y = \left[f(x) \right]^2$, then $y' =$

(A) $f^2(x)$ (B) $2f(x)$ (C) $f(x)f'(x)$

(D) $2f(x)f'(x)$ (E) $f^2(x)f'(x)$

---

6.   Find the horizontal asymptote for the function $f(x) = \dfrac{4x(4x+3)}{(4x+1)(4x+2)}$.

7. ■   The function $f(x) = \begin{cases} ax^3 \text{ , if } x \le 2 \\ 2x+k \text{ , if } x > 2 \end{cases}$ is differentiable at $x = 2$. Find a and k.

8. ■   For what interval of x is the curve $f(x) = \dfrac{2}{x^2 - 1}$ increasing and concave down?

9.   The point $(c, \, f(c))$ on the curve $f(x) = \sqrt{x}$ between $x = a = 0$ and $x = b = 4$ that satisfies $f'(c) = \dfrac{f(b) - f(a)}{b - a}$ is

      (A) $\left(\dfrac{1}{2}, \dfrac{\sqrt{2}}{2} \right)$ (B) $(1, \, 1)$ (C) $\left(2, \, \sqrt{2} \right)$ (D) $\left(3, \, \sqrt{3} \right)$

      (E)   none of the above

10.   How many values of x, such that $0 \le x \le \dfrac{\pi}{2}$, satisfy $\cos 2x + \cos x + 1 = 0$?

      (A) 0   (B) 1   (C) 2   (D) 3   (E) 4

11.   If the lines connecting the x- and y-intercepts of $y = a - x^2$ $(a > 0)$ form an equilateral triangle, find the value of a.

12.   The equations of all horizontal tangent lines to the curve $y^2 = \dfrac{x^2 + 4}{x}$ are

      (A) $x = 2$ only   (B) $y = 4$ only
      (C) $x = \pm 2$ (D) $y = \pm 2$
      (E)   none of the above

13. The position of a particle is given by $s = 2t^3 - 15t^2 + 24t + 5$ for $t \geq 0$. Find the total distance traveled by the particle in the first 5 seconds.

---

14. The function $y = x^{\frac{1}{3}}(x-2)^{\frac{2}{3}}$ has one relative minimum. That value of y is

(A) 0   (B) $\dfrac{1}{3}\sqrt[3]{4}$ (C) $\dfrac{2}{3}\sqrt[3]{4}$ (D) $\dfrac{2}{3}\sqrt[3]{2}$

(E)   none of the above

---

15. ■ A curve is defined by the equation $x^2 + y^2 = 25$ for $x \leq 4$ and by the equation $y = ax^2 + bx + \dfrac{29}{3}$ for $x > 4$. For what values of a and b will the relation be differentiable at the point (4, 3)?

---

16. ■ A spherical snowball is uniformly melting at the rate of $\dfrac{\pi}{18}$ in^3/min. At what rate is its diameter decreasing when its surface area is 3 in^2?

---

17. $\lim\limits_{x \to 0^+} x \ln \sqrt{x} =$

(A) $-\infty$ (B) -1 (C) 0   (D) 1   (E) ∞

---

18. If $y = e^{4x^2}$, then $\dfrac{d(\ln y)}{dx} =$

(A) $8x$ (B) $4x^2$ (C) $8xe^{4x^2}$ (D) $8xe^{8x}$ (E) $\dfrac{8x}{e^{4x^2}}$

---

19. Find the area of the region bounded by the x- and y-axes, the line $x = 1$, and the graph of $y = 2e^{3x}$.

20. If $x^2 - 2y^2 = 2$, then $\dfrac{d^2y}{dx^2}$ can be expressed in the form ay^b, where a and b are rational numbers in simplest form. Find a and b.

---

21. The volume of a solid generated by revolving the area bounded by $x = -1$, $x = 1$, and $y = e^{-x}$ about the x-axis is

(A) $\dfrac{1}{2}\pi e^2\left(1 - \dfrac{1}{e^4}\right)$

(B) $2\pi e^2\left(1 - \dfrac{1}{e^2}\right)$

(C) $\dfrac{1}{2}\pi e^2\left(1 - \dfrac{1}{e^2}\right)$

(D) $2\pi e^2\left(1 - \dfrac{1}{e^4}\right)$

(E) none of the above

---

22. If $y = \ln\left(x^x\right)$, then $y' =$

(A) $1 + \ln x$ (B) $y(1 + \ln x)$ (C) $x + \ln x$

(D) $y(x + \ln x)$ (E) $x \ln x$

---

23. ■

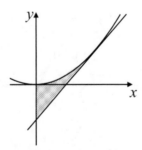

A line is drawn tangent to the curve $y = x^2$ at a point in the first quadrant. This tangent line, along with the curve and the y-axis, form a region whose area is equal to 9. Find the coordinates of the point of tangency.

---

24. ■ From a rest position a car accelerates at 4 meters/sec², then brakes decelerating at 6 meters/sec². It takes 5 seconds from the start to when it comes to a stop. How far had the car moved before the brakes were applied?

25. At what value of x $(x > 1)$ does the function $f(x) = \sqrt[x]{x}$ reaches its maximum?

26. If $f(x) = \ln(1 - 2\sin^2 x)$, then $f'\left(\dfrac{\pi}{8}\right) =$

    (A) -2 (B) $-\dfrac{\sqrt{2}}{2}$ (C) $\dfrac{\sqrt{2}}{2}$ (D) 1 (E) 2

27. An equation of the normal to the curve given parametrically as $\begin{cases} x = \cos^2 \theta \\ y = 2\sin\theta \end{cases}$

    at $\theta = \dfrac{\pi}{6}$ is

    (A) $4x + 8y + 5 = 0$ (B) $8x + 4y + 5 = 0$
    (C) $4x - 8y + 5 = 0$ (D) $8x - 4y + 5 = 0$
    (E) none of the above

28. $\displaystyle\int_1^e \dfrac{\ln x}{x^2}\,dx$ is

    (A) $1 - \dfrac{3\sqrt{e}}{2}$ (B) $1 - \dfrac{3}{e}$ (C) $1 - \dfrac{2}{e}$ (D) $1 - \dfrac{3}{2\sqrt{e}}$
    (E) none of the above

29. The function defined by $f(x) = \begin{cases} 2\pi\cos x + kx\ , \text{ if } x < \pi \\ 3x^2\ , \text{ if } x \geq \pi \end{cases}$ is continuous at $x = \pi$

    when $k =$

    (A) $3\pi - 2$ (B) $3\pi + 2$ (C) 6π (D) $3\pi^2 - 2\pi$ (E) $3\pi^2 + 2\pi$

30. The region bounded by the y-axis, $y = 8$, and the curve $y = x^3$ is divided into two regions by the line $y = a$. The area of the region from the x-axis to the line $y = a$ is $\dfrac{1}{3}$ the area of the region from $y = a$ to $y = 8$. The value of a is

(A) $2\sqrt[4]{2}$ (B) $2\sqrt[3]{2}$ (C) $2\sqrt[4]{3}$ (D) $2\sqrt{2}$ (E) 4

31. ■ $\dfrac{d}{dx} \displaystyle\int_2^x \dfrac{\ln t}{t^3}\, dt =$

(A) $\dfrac{1}{3x^2}$ (B) $\dfrac{\ln x}{x^3}$

(C) $\dfrac{\ln x - \ln 2}{x^3 - 8}$ (D) $\dfrac{\ln \dfrac{x}{2}}{x^3 - 2}$

(E) none of the above

32. ■ $C(n)$ is the total cost in dollars of producing n units of a certain commodity. $C'(n)$ (the rate of change of $C(n)$ with respect to n) is called the marginal cost and is used to approximate the cost of producing one more unit. If $C(n) = 0.02n^2 + 3n + 30$, determine the amount of error there is in using the marginal cost to approximate the cost of producing the 101-st unit.

1990

1. $\lim\limits_{x \to 0} \dfrac{1-2^{2x}}{1-2^x} =$

    (A) 0   (B) $\dfrac{1}{2}$ (C) 1   (D) 2   (E) ∞

2. When $x = y^2 + 3y + 2$ is solved for y, then $y =$

    (A) $\dfrac{-3 \pm \sqrt{1-4x}}{2}$ (B) $\dfrac{-3 \pm \sqrt{17-4x}}{2}$

    (C) $x^2 + 3x + 2$ (D) $-x^2 - 3x + 2$

    (E) none of the above

3.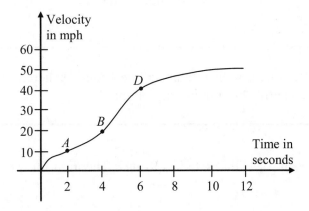

    What is the average acceleration from B to D. (Give answer in correct units.)

4. If $f(x) = 6x^2 + \dfrac{16}{x^2}$, then $\lim\limits_{h \to 0} \dfrac{f(2+h) - f(2)}{h} =$

    (A) 0   (B) 20   (C) 24   (D) 32   (E) ∞

5. If $f(x) = \sqrt{x-3}\sqrt{(x-2)^3}$, the values of x in the domain of f but not in the domain of f' are

    (A) only 2   (B) only 3   (C) 2 and 3   (D) 0, 2, and 3
    (E) none of the above

6. The curve $y = 3x^4 - 8x^3 + 6x^2 - 1$ has points of inflection at $x =$

    (A) 1 only   (B) -1 only

    (C) -1 and $-\dfrac{1}{3}$ (D) -1 and 1

    (E) 1 and $\dfrac{1}{3}$

7.■ The position s of a moving particle at time t is given by $s = \begin{cases} ct^2 \text{ , if } t \le 4 \\ 3t + d \text{ , if } t > 4 \end{cases}$. Find

    the constants c and d, if the path of motion and the velocity are both continuous at $t = 4$.

8.■ A right circular cone is to be circumscribed about a sphere of radius 1. Find the height of the cone that has minimum volume.

9. The value of c on [0, 1] that satisfies Rolle's Theorem for $f(x) = x - x^{\frac{1}{3}}$, is

    (A) $\dfrac{1}{27}$ (B) $\dfrac{\sqrt{3}}{9}$ (C) $\dfrac{1}{3}$ (D) $\dfrac{\sqrt{3}}{3}$ (E) $\dfrac{2}{3}\sqrt{3}$

10. A curve $y = f(x)$ is given by parametric equations $x = 2t^3 - 15t^2 + 24t + 7$ and
     $y = t^2 + 2t + 1$. The values of t at which the curve has a vertical tangent are

    (A) $t = -1$ only   (B) $t = -1$ and $t = 1$
    (C) $t = -1$ and $t = 4$ (D) $t = 1$ and $t = 4$
    (E) $t = -1$, $t = 1$, and $t = 4$

11. If $y = \dfrac{1}{4x}$, then $y' + y =$

   (A) $\dfrac{1}{4x}$ (B) $-\dfrac{1}{4x}$ (C) $-\dfrac{1}{4x^2}$ (D) $\dfrac{x+1}{4x^2}$ (E) $\dfrac{x-1}{4x^2}$

12. The graph of $f(x) = \dfrac{x^2 - x - 2}{2x^2 - x - 1}$ has a horizontal asymptote which it

   (A) crosses at $x = \dfrac{1}{2}$

   (B) crosses at $x = -\dfrac{1}{2}$

   (C) crosses at $x = 3$
   (D) crosses at $x = -3$
   (E) never intercepts

13. The curve $y = \dfrac{x+k}{x^2}$ has a relative minimum at $x = -8$. Find the value of the function at that point.

14.

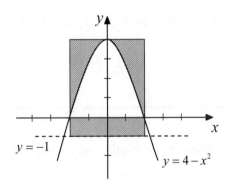

$y = -1$

$y = 4 - x^2$

Find the area of the shaded region in the figure above.

15.■ Find the two values of k such that $x + 3y = k$ is tangent to the ellipse $x^2 + 3y^2 = 1$.

16. ■ A snowman with a spherically molded head is uniformly melting at a rate of π in^3/hr. If its smile is $\dfrac{5}{8}$ the size of the head's diameter, at what rate is the smile melting when the volume of the head is 36π in^3?

---

17. Find a real number $x > 0$ for which $4x + \dfrac{9}{x}$ is the smallest.

---

18. $\dfrac{\ln 16}{3\ln 4 - 3\ln 2} =$

    (A) $\ln 2$ (B) 2   (C) $\dfrac{\ln 2}{\ln 8}$ (D) $\dfrac{4}{3}$

    (E) none of the above

---

19. The function $y = f(x)$ is given parametrically as $x = e^t$, $y = \ln t$. The natural domain of this function is

    (A) $x \geq 0$ (B) $x > 0$ (C) $x > 1$ (D) $x > e$

    (E) all real numbers

---

20. The slope of the tangent to the curve $y = x^x$ at the point (2, 4) is

    (A) $\ln 2 + 1$ (B) 4   (C) $4\ln 2$ (D) 8

    (E) none of the above

---

21. If $y = e^{nx}$, then $\dfrac{d^n y}{dx^n}$ (the n-th derivative of y with respect to x) is

    (A) $n! e^x$ (B) $n! e^{nx}$ (C) $n e^{nx}$ (D) $n^n e^x$ (E) $n^n e^{nx}$

---

22. The region enclosed by $y = \sqrt{x+3}$, $y = \sqrt{2x}$, and $y = 0$ is revolved about the x-axis. Find the volume of the solid formed.

23.■ All the triangles, in the first quadrant, formed by the x- and y-axes and any line tangent to the curve $y = \dfrac{1}{x}$ have the same area. What is that area?

24.■

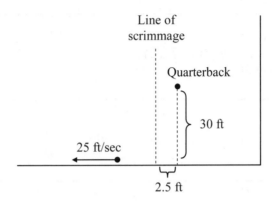

At a football game, at the instant the ball goes into play, a player at the line of scrimmage begins running along the edge of the field at a rate of 25 ft/sec. The quarterback receives the ball and is forced into a position 30 feet across the field from the boundary line along which the player is running, and $2\dfrac{1}{2}$ feet behind the line of scrimmage. $1\dfrac{1}{2}$ seconds later, the quarterback is poised to throw the ball.

At that instant, what is the rate at which the distance is changing from the quarterback to the player?

25. L'Hôpital's Rule states that if $\lim\limits_{x \to a} f(x) = 0$ and $\lim\limits_{x \to a} g(x) = 0$, then $\lim\limits_{x \to a} \dfrac{f(x)}{g(x)} = \lim\limits_{x \to a} \dfrac{f'(x)}{g'(x)}$. Find the positive constants c and d that make $\lim\limits_{x \to 0} \dfrac{\cos cx - d}{x^2} = -8$.

26. The area of the region bounded by $y = |x|$ and $y = 2 - x^2$ is

(A) $\dfrac{5}{3}$ (B) $\dfrac{7}{3}$ (C) $\dfrac{8}{3}$ (D) $\dfrac{10}{3}$ (E) $\dfrac{11}{3}$

27. If $\sin x = \dfrac{\tan x}{4} \neq 0$, then $\sin x \cdot \tan x =$

(A) $3\dfrac{1}{2}$ (B) $3\dfrac{3}{4}$ (C) 4 (D) $4\dfrac{1}{4}$ (E) $4\dfrac{1}{2}$

28. If $F(x) = \displaystyle\int_0^x \dfrac{1}{\sqrt{2t^3 + 20}}\,dt$, find $F'(2)$.

29. If $y = \sin u$, $u = e^v$, and $v = \sqrt{x}$, find the value of $\dfrac{dy}{dx}$ at $x = 1$.

30. Evaluate the integral $\displaystyle\int_0^{\frac{\pi}{4}} \dfrac{e^{\sqrt{\sec^2 x - 1}}}{1 - \sin^2 x}\,dx$.

31. ■ A function f has the property that its value at every real number x is equal to twice the slope of the tangent at that point. Also $f(0) = 1$. Find this function.

32. ■ Find the area of the region bounded by the graphs of $y = e^x$ and $y = \ln x$, the x- and y-axes, and the line segment joining the points $(1, e)$ and $(e, 1)$.

1989

1. $\lim\limits_{x\to 0}\dfrac{x^3+x^2-2x}{x^3-x}=$

   (A) −1   (B) 0   (C) 1   (D) 2   (E) ∞

---

2. If the function defined by $f(x)=\begin{cases} x^3\text{ , if } x\le 2 \\ 2x+k\text{ , if } x>2 \end{cases}$ is continuous at $x=2$,

   then $k=$

   (A) 0   (B) 2   (C) 4   (D) 6   (E) 8

---

3. The equation of the line tangent to the curve $f(x)=2x^3-3x^2$ at the point of inflection is

   (A) $y=0$ (B) $y=x$ (C) $y=-x$
   (D) $3x-2y=1$ (E) $6x+4y=1$

---

4. $\lim\limits_{h\to 0}\dfrac{\sqrt{2(6+h)-3}-\sqrt{2(6)-3}}{h}=$

   (A) $-\dfrac{1}{2}$ (B) 0   (C) $\dfrac{1}{3}$ (D) 6

   (E) none of the above

---

5. The number of horizontal asymptotes for the graph of the curve $y^2=\dfrac{2x}{x-1}$ is

   (A) 0   (B) 1   (C) 2   (D) 3   (E) 4

---

6. $f(x) = (2x-1)^{100}$. The tenth derivative of f, $f^{(10)}(x) = \dfrac{a!}{b!}2^c(2x-1)^d$. Find a, b, c, and d.

7. ■   If $f(x) = x-2$ and $g(f(x)) = 2x^2$, find $g(x)$.

8. ■   Two sandboxes are being constructed in a small playground. One is to have the shape of a regular hexagon, and the other that of an equilateral triangle. The total length of board used to make the sides is 60 ft. For what length of a side of the hexagon the total playing area is the smallest?

9. $f'(x) = 3x^2 - 2x + 1$ and the graph of $f(x)$ contains the point $(2, 2)$. Find $f(x)$.

10.   Given: $f(5) = 4$; $f'(5) = 2$; $g(3) = 5$; $g'(3) = 7$. Find the derivative of $f(g(x))$ at $x = 3$.

11.   The area bounded by the curves $y = 4 - x^2$ and $y = (x-2)^2$ is

     (A) 0   (B) $\dfrac{4}{3}$ (C) 2   (D) $\dfrac{8}{3}$ (E) $\dfrac{16}{3}$

12.   For which of the following curves in the xy-plane the slope of the tangent line at every point equals $-\dfrac{2x}{y}$?

     (A)   straight line
     (B)   circle
     (C)   ellipse
     (D)   hyperbola
     (E)   parabola

13. The value of $\int_0^3 \left| x^2 - 3x + 2 \right| dx$ is

   (A) $\dfrac{3}{2}$ (B) $\dfrac{5}{3}$ (C) $\dfrac{11}{6}$ (D) $\dfrac{5}{2}$ (E) $\dfrac{7}{3}$

14. If $f(x) = 2x^3$, $a = 0$, $b = 3$, and $f(b) - f(a) = (b-a)f'(c)$, then the value of c in the interval $[0, 3]$ is

   (A) $\sqrt{2}$ (B) $\sqrt{3}$ (C) 2   (D) 3   (E) 18

15. ∎ The surface area of a cube is increasing at a rate of 12 in²/sec. How fast is the volume of the cube increasing at the instant when the surface area is 24 in²?

16. ∎ The curve $3y = x^3 - 5$ has both the tangent line and the normal line drawn to it at the point where $x = -1$. Find the two points on the normal line which are $\sqrt{10}$ units away from where the tangent line crosses the x-axis.

17. $\displaystyle \lim_{x \to \infty} \dfrac{\tan \dfrac{4}{x}}{\dfrac{1}{x}} =$

   (A) -4 (B) 0   (C) 1   (D) ∞
   (E) none of the above

18. $\ln \tan 20° + \ln \cot 20° =$

   (A) 0   (B) 1   (C) e (D) π (E) ∞

19. $f(x) = \sin^2 x$. If $f'''(x) = a \sin 2x$, then $a =$

(A) -8 (B) -4 (C) -2 (D) 2 (E) 8

20. At what point on the curve $y = e^{-x}$ does the tangent to the curve pass through the origin?

21. The area of the triangle formed by the two axes and the line tangent to the curve $y = \sin 2x$ at $x = \dfrac{\pi}{2}$ is

(A) $\dfrac{\pi}{4}$ (B) $\dfrac{\pi}{2}$ (C) $\dfrac{\pi^2}{8}$ (D) $\dfrac{\pi^2}{4}$ (E) $\dfrac{\pi^2}{2}$

22. $\log_a b \cdot \log_b a =$

(A) 1 (B) $a+b$ (C) ab (D) $\dfrac{a}{b}$

(E) none of the above

23. ▪ The region bounded by $y = \dfrac{1}{\sqrt{x}}$, $y = 0$, $x = 1$, and $x = 9$ is to be divided by two vertical lines $x = a$ and $x = b$ $(1 < a < b < 9)$ into three regions equal in area. Find the value of a.

24. ▪ A train is just starting to move with a constant acceleration of 0.5 m/sec^2. At that moment, a man at a certain distance d from the nearest entry door of the train is running at a constant speed of 6 m/sec. What can the largest value of d be for the man still to catch the train?

25. For the function $f(x) = \ln(x^2 - 1)$, $\dfrac{f(7) - f(5)}{f'(7) - f'(5)} =$

 (A) $-8 \ln 2$ (B) $-8 \ln 24$ (C) $-12 \ln 2$ (D) $-12 \ln 24$ (E) $-6 \ln 24$

26. If $\cos 20° = k$ and $\cos x = 2k^2 - 1$, what are all the possible values of x between $0°$ and $360°$?

27. The equation of the tangent to the curve $\ln y = 3x^2 + 6x$ at the point where $x = 0$ is

 (A) $y = 6x + 1$ (B) $y = 6x + 6$

 (C) $y = 6xy + 6$ (D) $y = \dfrac{6x}{y} + 6$

 (E) none of the above

28. If the y-coordinate at each point of inflection on the curve $y = e^{-x^2}$ is $\dfrac{1}{e^a}$, then $a =$

 (A) -1 (B) $-\dfrac{1}{2}$ (C) 1 (D) $\dfrac{1}{2}$ (E) 2

29. If $f(x) = x \ln x$, then $f(2) + f'(2) + f''(2) + f'''(2) =$

 (A) $2 \ln 2 + \dfrac{5}{4}$ (B) $\ln 8 + \dfrac{5}{4}$ (C) $\ln 4 + \dfrac{3}{2}$ (D) $\ln 8 + \dfrac{3}{4}$

 (E) none of the above

30. Find the volume of the solid generated when the curve bounded by $y = \sin\left(x - \dfrac{\pi}{6}\right)$ and the x-axis from $x = \dfrac{\pi}{6}$ to $x = \dfrac{2\pi}{3}$ is rotated about the x-axis.

31.■ A particle moves along the x-axis so that its x-coordinate at any time t is $x = ce^{kt} + de^{-kt}$. Its acceleration is $a = 2x$. Find the value of k, if $k > 0$.

32.■ Find the total area bounded by the curves $y = \sqrt{x}$ and $y = -\ln x$ between the lines $x = 1$ and $x = 4$.

1988

1. $\displaystyle\lim_{x \to 10} \frac{3x^2 - 7x + 10}{60 + 3x^2} =$

   (A) −1   (B) $\dfrac{2}{3}$ (C) 1   (D) 10   (E) ∞

2. If $f(x) = 2^x$ and $g(x) = \dfrac{x+1}{x}$, then $f\big(g(-2)\big) =$

   (A) $\dfrac{1}{5}$ (B) $\dfrac{1}{2\sqrt{2}}$ (C) $\dfrac{1}{\sqrt{2}}$ (D) $\sqrt{2}$ (E) 5

3. The sum of the roots of $9x^3 + 18x^2 - x - 10 = 0$ is

   (A) −2   (B) −1   (C) 0   (D) 1   (E) 2

4. The graph of $y = \dfrac{3x}{1 + |x|}$ has the following number of vertical and horizontal asymptotes:

   (A) no vertical and one horizontal
   (B) no vertical and two horizontal
   (C) one vertical and one horizontal
   (D) two vertical and no horizontal
   (E) two vertical and two horizontal

5. The graph of $f(x) = -\dfrac{x}{1-x^2}$ has

 (A) symmetry about the x-axis
 (B) symmetry about the y-axis
 (C) symmetry about the origin
 (D) symmetry about $y = x$
 (E) none of the above

---

6. The sum of a positive number plus twice a second positive number is 18. If these two numbers were to yield a maximum product, the smaller of the two numbers is

 (A) $\dfrac{5}{2}$ (B) $\dfrac{7}{2}$ (C) $\dfrac{9}{2}$ (D) $\dfrac{11}{2}$

 (E) none of the above

7.■ Which of the following lines is tangent to the graph of $f(x) = \dfrac{x^3}{3} - \dfrac{3}{2}x^2 + x$ and perpendicular to $y = x$?

 (A) $x + y = 5$ (B) $2x + 2y = 3$
 (C) $3x + 3y = 2$ (D) $4x + 4y = 7$
 (E) $5x + 5y = 6$

8.■ $f(x) = \begin{cases} cx^2 + \dfrac{9}{2}, & \text{if } x < 3 \\ ax + b, & \text{if } x \geq 3 \end{cases}$. The slope of the line tangent to the graph of $f(x)$ at $x = -1$ is 1. Find the values of a, b, and c such that $f'(x)$ is defined over the domain of f.

---

9. Consider the curve $f(x) = x^2$ from $x_1 = 3$ to $x_2 = 6$. Find c, where $x_1 \leq c \leq x_2$, such that $f(c)(x_2 - x_1) = \displaystyle\int_{x_1}^{x_2} f(x)\,dx$.

10. The derivative of $y = (6x-4)^2(3x-2)^3$ can be written as

   (A) $60(3x-2)^4$ (B) $30(6x-4)(3x-2)^2$
   (C) $18(6x-4)^2(3x-2)$ (D) $60(6x-4)^4$
   (E) $30(6x-4)(3x-2)$

---

11. The area bounded by the curves $y = \sqrt{x}$ and $y = x^n$ $(n>1)$ is

   (A) $\dfrac{2n-1}{3n+3}$ (B) $\dfrac{3n-1}{2n+3}$ (C) $\dfrac{2n+3}{3n-1}$ (D) $\dfrac{2n+1}{3n-3}$ (E) $\dfrac{3n+1}{2n-3}$

---

12. Consider the function $f(x) = x^{\frac{4}{3}} + 4x^{\frac{1}{3}}$ on the interval $-8 \le x \le 8$. Find the coordinates of the point at which the tangent to the curve is a horizontal line.

---

13. Let f be defined by $f(x) = \begin{cases} ax+b, & \text{if } x < 2 \\ x^2+x+1, & \text{if } x \ge 2 \end{cases}$. Find the values of a and b such that f is differentiable at $x = 2$.

---

14. If $f(x) = \dfrac{x}{x+1}$, then $f^{-1}(x)$ can be expressed as

   (A) $f(x)$ (B) $\dfrac{f(x)}{x}$ (C) $f(x)\dfrac{x}{1-x}$

   (D) $f(x)\dfrac{1+x}{1-x}$ (E) $f(x)\dfrac{1-x}{1+x}$

---

15. ■ Find the points on the curve $xy + 4x - 3y^2 = 27$ where the tangents to the curve are vertical lines.

16.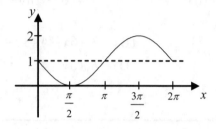

The graph of $y = 1 - \sin x$ over $0 \le x \le 2\pi$ is shown above. Sketch the graph of the curve $y(1 - \sin x) = 1$ over $0 \le x \le 2\pi$.

17. If $x = \dfrac{1}{e}$, then x^x can be written as

(A) 1   (B) e (C) $\sqrt[e]{e}$ (D) $\dfrac{1}{\sqrt[e]{e}}$

(E) none of the above

18. If the derivative of $\dfrac{f(x)}{x}$ is $\dfrac{f(x)(x-1)}{x^2}$, then

(A) $f(x) = f'(x)$ (B) $f(x) = -f'(x)$

(C) $f(x) = \dfrac{f'(x)}{2}$ (D) $f(x) = 2f'(x)$

(E) $f(x) = -2f'(x)$

19. A particle moves along the x-axis where its velocity at any time $t > 1$ is given by $v = \dfrac{2t+3}{t^2+3t-4}$. The total number of units the particle travels from $t = 2$ to $t = 4$ is

(A) $\ln 6$ (B) $\ln 8$ (C) 2   (D) 4

(E) none of the above

20. If $f(x)$ is an even function and if $\displaystyle\int_0^2 f(x)\,dx = K$, then express

$\displaystyle\int_{-2}^0 3f(x)\,dx + \int_{-2}^2 f(x)\,dx$ in terms of K.

21. Find the coordinates of the relative maximum for the curve

$$f(x) = \begin{cases} x^2 - 2 \text{ , if } x < 2 \\ 4 - x \text{ , if } x \geq 2 \end{cases}$$

---

22. Find the coordinates of the three points on the curve $y = x^2 - 2$ where the normal to the curve passes through the origin.

---

23. ■ Suppose $g(x)$ is the x-intercept of the line joining the points $(0, h)$ and $\left(\dfrac{h^2}{6}, \sqrt{h^2 - \dfrac{h^4}{36}} \right)$. Find $\lim\limits_{x \to 0^+} g(x)$.

---

24. ■ The area of the region bounded by the two axes and the line tangent to the graph of $f(x) = x \ln x$ at $x = e$ is

(A) $\dfrac{e}{4}$ (B) $\dfrac{e}{2}$ (C) $\dfrac{e^2}{4}$ (D) $\dfrac{e^2}{2}$

(E)   none of the above

---

25. $\arcsin x + \arccos x =$

(A) $-\pi$ (B) $-\dfrac{\pi}{2}$ (C) 0   (D) $\dfrac{\pi}{2}$ (E) π

---

26. If $f(x) = 4x - 8$ and $f(g(x)) = 2x^2$, find a formula for $g(x)$.

---

27. The slope of the line tangent to the curve $y = \dfrac{\tan x}{\cos x}$ at $x = \dfrac{\pi}{3}$ is

(A) -8 (B) $2\sqrt{3}$ (C) $3\sqrt{2}$ (D) 8   (E) 14

28. The graph of $f(x) = xe^x$

    (A) is always concave up
    (B) is always concave down
    (C) has one inflection point
    (D) has two inflection points
    (E) has more than two inflection points

29. If $y = \sin x$, then the derivative of y with respect to $3x - 1$ is

    (A) $\cos x$ (B) $\dfrac{\cos x}{3}$ (C) $3 \cos x$ (D) $\cos \dfrac{x}{3}$ (E) $\cos 3x$

30. There are two regions bounded by $x^2 + 2xy + y^2 = 1$ and the x and y axes. The total area of these two regions is

    (A) 2 (B) 4 (C) 6 (D) 8
    (E) none of the above

31.■ Find the area of the region bounded by $y = \ln x$, $y = \ln \sqrt{x}$, and $x = e$.

32.■ Two parallel sides of a rectangle are increasing in length at the rate of 4 in/min. The other two sides are decreasing in length so that the area of the rectangle remains constant equal 80 in². Find the rate at which a side decreasing in length is changing at the instant a side increasing in length is 10 inches.

1987

1. An odd function is symmetric about the

   (A) y-axis
   (B) x-axis
   (C) line $y = x$
   (D) line $y = -x$
   (E) origin

---

2. The inverse of the function $y = x^2 - 2x + 3$ is

   (A) $y = x - 1$ (B) $y = 1 \pm \sqrt{x-2}$

   (C) $y = 2 \pm \sqrt{x-1}$ (D) $y = 3 \pm \sqrt{x}$

   (E) $y = \sqrt{x^2 - 2x + 3}$

---

3. The expression $\dfrac{(x+1)(2x+1) - (x^2 + x)}{(x+1)^2}$, $x \neq -1$, can be simplified to

   (A) 1   (B) 2   (C) $\dfrac{x+1-x^2}{x+1}$ (D) $\dfrac{2x+1-x^2}{x+1}$

   (E) none of the above

---

4. If $f(x) = ax^2 + bx + c$ $(a > 0)$ and m is the minimum value of this function, then
   $f\left(\dfrac{-b}{2a} + 1\right) - m =$

   (A) a (B) b (C) c (D) $-b$ (E) 0

5.

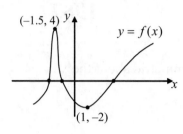

In the figure above, the values of x that yield negative outputs are

(A) $x > 0$

(B) $x > -1$

(C) $-\dfrac{3}{2} < x < 1$

(D) $-2 < x < 4$

(E) $x < -2$ or $-1 < x < 3$

6.   If $f(x) = \sqrt{x^2}$, $f'(0)$ is

(A) -1 (B) 0 (C) 1 (D) 2
(E)   non-existent

7.■   An equation for the line tangent to the curve $f(x) = -x^3 + 12x + 5$ at the point of inflection is

(A) $12x - y = 3$

(B) $y - 12x = 3$

(C) $12x - y = 5$

(D) $y - 12x = 5$

(E) $12x - y = 35$

8.■

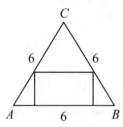

Find the dimensions of the rectangle of the greatest area that can be inscribed in an equilateral triangle with side 6, as shown above.

9. The distance from the point (a, b) to the line $x = c$ is

(A) $|b-a|$ (B) $|a-c|$ (C) $|b-c|$ (D) $|x-a+c|$ (E) $|x-a-c|$

---

10. The graph of $(x+4)^2 = -(y-3)^3$ has

(A) a point of inflection at $x = -4$
(B) a minimum at $x = -4$
(C) no maximum
(D) no minimum
(E) a horizontal asymptote $y = 0$

---

11. If $f(x) = 3^x$ and $f(k) = \dfrac{f(x+1)}{f(x-1)}$, then $k =$

(A) 1   (B) 2   (C) 3   (D) 6   (E) 9

---

12. $\lim\limits_{h \to 0} \dfrac{4(2+h)^3 - 2(2+h) - 28}{h} =$

(A) 0   (B) 26   (C) 28   (D) 36
(E) none of the above

---

13. For the curve $x^3 - 2xy + y^2 = 5$, the slope of the tangent to the curve at $(2, 3)$ is

(A) -3 (B) $-\dfrac{3}{5}$ (C) 0   (D) $\dfrac{3}{5}$ (E) 3

---

14. Given $f(x) = \sqrt{x}$, a value for c such that $f(b) = f'(c)(b-a) + f(a)$ for $a = 4$ and $b = 9$ is

(A) $3\dfrac{7}{8}$ (B) $4\dfrac{3}{4}$ (C) $5\dfrac{3}{8}$ (D) $6\dfrac{1}{4}$ (E) $7\dfrac{1}{2}$

15. ■ The line tangent to the curve $f(x) = \frac{1}{2}x^3 + \frac{3}{2}x^2 + 2x + 5$ at $x = -2$ intersects the curve only once again. Find the area bounded by the tangent line and the curve.

---

16. ■ Water is running out of a conical container 12 ft in diameter and 8 ft deep (vertex down) and filling a spherical balloon. At the instant the depth of the water in the cone is 4 ft, the radius of the sphere is approximately 4 ft. Find the ratio of the rate of change of the depth of water in the cone to the rate of change of the radius of the balloon at that instant.

---

17. If $x = \ln x^2$, $x \neq 0$, and $g(x) = \sin x$, then the derivative of $g(f(x))$ is

(A) $\tan x^2$

(B) $\cos\left(\ln\left(x^2\right)\right)$

(C) $\dfrac{2\sin x \cos x}{\sin^2 x}$

(D) $\dfrac{2\cos\left(\ln\left(x^2\right)\right)}{x}$

(E) $\dfrac{2x\ln(\cos x)}{\sin x}$

---

18. The range of the function $y = 10^{-3\log_{10} e^{\ln x}}$ is

(A) $y > 0$
(B) $y > 1$
(C) $0 < y < 1$
(D) all real numbers
(E) all real numbers, except $y = 0$

---

19. $\lim\limits_{x \to 4} \dfrac{\sqrt{3x+4} - \sqrt{2x+8}}{x-4} =$

(A) 0 (B) $\dfrac{1}{8}$ (C) $\dfrac{1}{4}$ (D) $\dfrac{1}{2}$ (E) undefined

20. If $f(x) = x^e e^x$, then $f'(x) =$

    (A) $x^e e^x$ (B) $x^{e-1} e^{x-1}$

    (C) $e^x \left(ex^e + x^e \right)$ (D) $\dfrac{x^e (e+x)}{xe^x}$

    (E) $\dfrac{x^e e^x (x+e)}{x}$

---

21. Find an equation of the line tangent to the graph of $\begin{cases} x = t^2 + t \\ y = t^2 - t \end{cases}$ at $t = -\dfrac{1}{2}$.

---

22. For the curve $y = x^2$, let m represent the slope of the tangent to the curve at any point on the curve. Then the coordinates for any point (x, y) on the curve can be correctly represented as

    (A) $\left(\dfrac{m}{4}, \dfrac{m^2}{2} \right)$ (B) $\left(\dfrac{m}{2}, \dfrac{m^2}{4} \right)$ (C) $\left(m, \dfrac{m}{2} \right)$ (D) $\left(m, m^2 \right)$ (E) $\left(2m, 4m^2 \right)$

---

23. ▪ The average value of the function $y = x^2 + 4$ over the interval from a to b is 25. Find the value of $a^2 + ab + b^2$.

---

24. ▪ Find the area of the region bounded by the line tangent to the hyperbola $x^2 - y^2 = 16$ at $(5, 3)$ and the two asymptotes, $y = \pm x$, of the hyperbola.

---

25. $\lim\limits_{h \to 0} \dfrac{\sin\left(\dfrac{\pi}{3} + 2h \right)}{h} =$

    (A) -1 (B) $-\dfrac{1}{2}$ (C) 0 (D) $\dfrac{1}{2}$ (E) 1

26. $F(x) = \int_0^x \dfrac{1}{\sqrt{2t^3 - 7}}\, dt$. Find $F'(2)$.

27. If the period of $f(x) = \dfrac{1}{k}\cos(4\pi kx)$ is 6, then the amplitude of this function is

(A) 4 (B) $\dfrac{3\pi}{2}$ (C) 6 (D) 2π (E) 12

28. The area of an ellipse is given by the formula $A = \pi ab$, where a represents $\dfrac{1}{2}$ the length of the major axis and b represents $\dfrac{1}{2}$ the length of the minor axis. The area of the ellipse $\dfrac{x^2}{a^2} + \dfrac{y^2}{16} = 1$ is 8π more than the area of the circle $x^2 + y^2 = 16$. Find the length of the major axis of the ellipse.

29. If $x = e^{\sqrt{t}}$ and $y = e^{-\sqrt{t}}$, the range of the function $y = y(x)$ given by these parametric equations for $t > 0$ is

(A) $y > 0$ (B) $y \geq 1$
(C) $0 < y < 1$ (D) $0 < y \leq 1$
(E) all real numbers

30. Find the approximate value of $\sqrt{9 - \sin 2x}$ at $x = 0.06$ (to the nearest hundredth) by using linear approximation.

31.■ $y = 3u^2$, $u = e^v$, and $v = \sqrt{2 - x}$. Express $\dfrac{dy}{dx}$ when $x = 1$ in simplest terms.

32.■ Find the volume of the solid generated when the graph of $f(x) = \sqrt{x}\sin x$ over the interval $0 \leq x \leq \pi$ is revolved about the x-axis.

1. If $g(x) = \sin x$ and $f(g(x)) = 3^{\sin x}$, then the range of $f(x)$ is

    (A) $y < 0$

    (B) $-1 \le y \le 1$

    (C) $\dfrac{1}{3} \le y \le 3$

    (D) $y > 0$

    (E) all real numbers

---

2. What value must be assigned to $f\left(\dfrac{1}{2}\right)$ if $f(x) = \dfrac{2x^2 + 5x - 3}{2x^2 - 9x + 4}$ is to be continuous at $x = \dfrac{1}{2}$?

---

3. $\displaystyle\lim_{h \to 0} \dfrac{\sqrt{9 + h} - 3}{h} =$

    (A) 0

    (B) $\dfrac{1}{6}$

    (C) $\dfrac{1}{3}$

    (D) 3

    (E) 6

4.

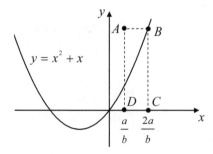

    In the figure above, the area of rectangle $ABCD$ is

    (A) $\dfrac{4a}{b}$

    (B) $\dfrac{4a^3 + 2a^2 b}{b^3}$

    (C) $\dfrac{4a^2 + 2ab}{b^2}$

    (D) $\dfrac{2a^3 + 4a^2 b}{b^3}$

    (E) $\dfrac{2a^3 + 2a^2 b}{b^3}$

---

5. If $f(x)=\sqrt{1-\dfrac{2}{x}}$ and $g(x)=\dfrac{1}{x}$, then the derivative of $f\big(g(x)\big)$, evaluated at $x=-4$ is

   (A) $-\dfrac{1}{3}$ (B) $-\dfrac{1}{9}$ (C) $\dfrac{1}{9}$ (D) $\dfrac{1}{3}$ (E) 1

6. The values of x for which the function $f(x)=\dfrac{x}{1+x^2}$ increases is

   (A) $x>1$ or $x<1$ (B) $-1<x<1$ (C) $0<x<1$
   (D) all real numbers   (E) the empty set

7.■ Two tangents can be drawn to the curve $y=x^2-7$ from the point $(3,-2)$. The sum of the slopes of these 2 tangent lines is

   (A) 2   (B) 6   (C) 8   (D) 12
   (E) none of the above

8.■ Find the coordinates of all the points of inflection for the graph of $y=9x^{\frac{1}{3}}+x^2$.

9. If $f(x)=\begin{cases}1\text{, if }x\le-2\\ x^2-4\text{, if }-2<x<2,\\ x\text{, if }x\ge2\end{cases}$ the range of f is

   (A) $y\ge-4$ (B) $y\ge1$
   (C) $y=1$ or $y\ge2$ (D) $-4\le y<0$ or $y=1$ or $y\ge2$
   (E) all real numbers

10. If $f(x)=\sqrt{2x+7}$, where $F'(x)=f(x)$ and $F(1)=7$, then $F(x)=$

(A) $\dfrac{1}{\sqrt{2x+7}}$

(B) $\dfrac{1}{2\sqrt{2x+7}}$

(C) $\dfrac{1}{3}(2x+7)^{\frac{3}{2}}-2$

(D) $\dfrac{2}{3}(2x+7)^{\frac{3}{2}}-11$

(E) $\sqrt{2x+7}+4$

11. $[x]$ represents the greatest integer that does not exceed x. $\displaystyle\lim_{x\to2^-}\dfrac{x-[x]}{[x-3]}=$

(A) -1 (B) $-\dfrac{1}{2}$ (C) 0 (D) $\dfrac{1}{2}$ (E) 1

12. An equation for the line tangent to the curve $2x^2-y^4=1$ at the point $(-1,1)$ is

(A) $y=-x$

(B) $y=-x-2$

(C) $y=-\dfrac{3}{4}(x+1)+1$

(D) $y=-\dfrac{1}{2}(x+1)+1$

(E) $y=-\dfrac{1}{2}(x-1)-1$

13. Suppose $f(x)=bc^x$ and it is also true that $f(x)=c^{x-1}$. If $f\left(\dfrac{5}{2}\right)=27$, the value of $c-2b$ is

(A) $\dfrac{39}{5}$ (B) $\dfrac{49}{6}$ (C) $\dfrac{59}{7}$ (D) $\dfrac{69}{8}$ (E) $\dfrac{79}{9}$

14. A particle moves along the x-axis and its velocity is given by $v=4\sqrt{t}$. At $t=9$, $x=50$. Find the position of the particle at the time its acceleration is 1.

15. ■ A rectangle with a perimeter of 24 inches is rotated about one of its sides to generate a right circular cylinder. Find the area of the rectangle with the given perimeter that will generate the largest possible volume for the cylinder.

---

16. ■ A right isosceles triangle maintains its shape as it increases in size. How fast is the area changing at the instant the hypotenuse is 7 ft and is increasing at the rate of 10 ft/hr?

---

17. If $y = x - 1$, $x > 1$, then $\dfrac{d^2(\ln y)}{dx^2} =$

(A) 0   (B) $\dfrac{1}{x-1}$ (C) $-\dfrac{1}{x-1}$ (D) $\dfrac{1}{(x-1)^2}$ (E) $-\dfrac{1}{(x-1)^2}$

---

18. The range of $y = 1 - e^{-x}$ is

(A) $y < 1$ (B) $y \le 1$ (C) $y > 1$ (D) all real numbers
(E) none of the above

---

19. $\displaystyle\lim_{h \to 0} \dfrac{e^6 \left(e^{3h} - 1 \right)}{h} =$

(A) 0   (B) ∞ (C) e^6 (D) $3e^6$
(E) none of the above

---

20. Find an antiderivative of $\dfrac{\sqrt[3]{x^2} - \sqrt[4]{x}}{\sqrt{x}}$.

---

21. If $y = 5xe^{\ln 7}$, then $y' =$

(A) $5 \ln 7$ (B) 35   (C) $35e^{\ln 7}$ (D) $5 + xe^{\ln 7}$ (E) $5xe^{\ln 7} + 5$

22. The function $f(x) = \dfrac{e^{-x+1} - 1}{\ln x}$ is defined for all $x > 0$ except $x = 1$. The value that must be assigned to $f(1)$ to make $f(x)$ continuous at $x = 1$ is

(A) -1 (B) $-\dfrac{1}{e}$ (C) 0 (D) $\dfrac{1}{e}$ (E) 1

23. ■ Find the coordinates of the minimum point for the curve $y = x^x$, $x > 0$.

24. ■ Find the volume generated by revolving the area bounded by $y = -x^3$, $y = 0$, and $x = -2$ about the line $x = 1$.

25. Find $\lim\limits_{x \to \frac{\pi}{2}} \dfrac{\sin^3 x - 1}{1 - \sin x}$.

26. If $f(x) = \sqrt{\ln x}$, $x \geq 1$, the domain of $f'(x)$ is

(A) $0 < x \leq 1$ (B) $x > 1$ (C) $x \geq 1$
(D) the empty set   (E) all real numbers

27. The function $f(x) = \dfrac{x^3 - 8}{x - 2}$ is not defined at $x = 2$. Which of the following expressions for $f(2)$ can be used to make $f(x)$ continuous at $x = 2$?

I. $f(2) = 12$ II. $f(2) = \lim\limits_{x \to 2} f(x)$ III. $f(2) = \lim\limits_{x \to 2^-} f(x)$

(A) I only   (B) II only   (C) I and II
(D) II and III   (E) I, II, and III

28. The average value of $\sec^2 x$ over the interval from $x = \dfrac{\pi}{6}$ to $x = \dfrac{\pi}{3}$ is

(A) $\dfrac{2\sqrt{3}}{3\pi}$ (B) $\dfrac{2\sqrt{3}}{3}$ (C) $\dfrac{4\sqrt{3}}{\pi}$ (D) $\dfrac{20}{9}$ (E) $\dfrac{8}{3}$

29. A particle moves along the x-axis starting at the origin at $t = 0$ with acceleration given by $a(t) = -6t$. Find its velocity at $t = 0$ if the maximum displacement of the particle in the positive direction is 16 units.

30. A curve is given parametrically by the equations $x = t$, $y = 1 - \cos t$. Find the area bounded by the curve and the x-axis on the interval $0 \le t \le 2\pi$.

31.■ Both the tangent line and the normal line are drawn to the curve $4y = x^2$ at the point where $x = 2$. Find the coordinates of the two points on the normal line which are 10 units away from the point where the tangent line crosses the x-axis.

32.■ Evaluate $\displaystyle\int_{-\pi}^{\pi}\left[x^2 \sin x + x + 1\right] dx$.

1985

1. If $f(x) = 3x - 2$ and $f(g(x)) = 6x + 25$, then $g(x) =$

   (A) $2x + 9$ (B) $3x + 23$ (C) $9x + 27$ (D) $18x + 13$
   (E) none of the above

2.

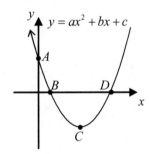

In the figure above, the sum of the x-coordinates of the four points A, B, C, and D is

   (A) 0 (B) $\dfrac{-b}{a}$ (C) $\dfrac{-b}{2a}$ (D) $\dfrac{-3b}{2a}$

   (E) none of the above

---

3. $\lim\limits_{x \to \pi} \dfrac{x^2 - \pi^2}{3 - \dfrac{3x}{\pi}} =$

   (A) $-\dfrac{2}{3}\pi^2$ (B) -3 (C) 0 (D) 3 (E) $2\pi^2$

---

4. The graph of $y = \dfrac{2x^2}{4 - x^2}$ has

    (A) no horizontal or vertical asymptotes
    (B) one vertical asymptote and no horizontal asymptotes
    (C) no vertical asymptotes and one horizontal asymptote
    (D) two vertical asymptotes and one horizontal asymptote
    (E) two horizontal asymptotes and one vertical asymptote

5. Find the minimum value of $f(x) = x^3 - 3x + 2$ over the interval $\left[-3, \dfrac{3}{2}\right]$.

6. If $f(x) = \dfrac{ax - b}{cx - a}$, $c \neq 0$, $b \neq \dfrac{a^2}{c}$, $x \neq \dfrac{a}{c}$, then $f^{-1}(x) =$

    (A) $f(x)$ (B) $f(-x)$ (C) $-f(x)$ (D) $-f(-x)$
    (E) none of the above

7.■ The curve $y = ax + \dfrac{b}{x}$ has a relative minimum at the point $(1, 4)$. Find the values of a and b.

8.■ Find the equations of the tangent lines to the curve $y = x^4 + 2x^3 + 3x - 5$ at all points of inflection.

9. The range of the function $y = \dfrac{2x}{x - 5}$ is

    (A) $y \leq -2$ (B) $y \geq 0$ (C) $y > 2$ (D) $y \neq 2$
    (E) all real numbers

10. If $S(t)$ is the surface area and $V(t)$ is the volume of a sphere, then $\dfrac{dV}{dt} =$

(A) $\dfrac{r}{2}\dfrac{dS}{dt}$ (B) $2r\dfrac{dS}{dt}$ (C) $4r^2\dfrac{dS}{dt}$ (D) $\dfrac{r^2}{4}\dfrac{dS}{dt}$ (E) $2r^2\dfrac{dS}{dt}$

11. $\displaystyle\lim_{h\to 0}\dfrac{(2+h)^4 - 3(2+h) - 10}{h} =$

(A) 0 (B) 15 (C) 26 (D) 29 (E) 32

12. The slope of the line normal to the curve $xy + x - 2y + 2 = 0$ at the point where $x = 4$ is

(A) -2 (B) -1 (C) 0 (D) $\dfrac{1}{2}$ (E) 1

13. If $f(x) = x^3$, $a = 0$, $b = 6$, and $f(b) - f(a) = (b-a)f'(c)$, then the value of c is

(A) 2 (B) $2\sqrt{2}$ (C) $2\sqrt{3}$ (D) $2\sqrt{6}$
(E) none of the above

14. A particle moves along the x-axis where its acceleration is given by $a(t) = 6t + 6$. Given that $v = 15$ at $t = 2$, find the total distance the particle travels from $t = 0$ to $t = 2$.

15.■ A function is defined for $-2 < x < 2$ by $f(x) = \begin{cases} 5x^2 + ax + b \text{, if } -2 < x \leq 0 \\ (2x+4)^{\frac{5}{2}} \text{, if } 0 < x < 2 \end{cases}$.

Find the values of a and b if $f(x)$ is differentiable at $x = 0$.

16.■ Find the area bounded by the curve $y^2 = x + 1$ and the line $x - 2y - 2 = 0$.

17. $\sin 0° + \sin 10° + \sin 20° + \sin 30° + ... + \sin 340° + \sin 350° + \sin 360° =$

   (A) 0   (B) $\sqrt{2}$ (C) 2   (D) π (E) 2π

18. What value should be assigned to $f(x) = \dfrac{x}{e^x - 1}$ at $x = 0$ to make $f(x)$ continuous at $x = 0$?

   (A) -1 (B) 0   (C) $\dfrac{1}{2}$ (D) 1

   (E) none of the above

19. If $f(x) = 1 + \ln(x + 2)$, $f^{-1}(x) =$

   (A) $e^{x-1} - 2$ (B) $e^{x+1} - 2$ (C) $e^{x-1} + 2$ (D) $e^{x+1} + 2$
   (E) none of the above

20. The slope of the line normal to the curve $y = xe^{x^3}$ at $x = 1$ is

   (A) $-\dfrac{4}{e}$ (B) $-\dfrac{e}{4}$ (C) $-\dfrac{1}{4e}$ (D) $\dfrac{4}{e}$ (E) $4e$

21. The acceleration of a particle is given by $a(t) = \cos t - \sin t$. At $t = 0$, velocity $v = 1$. During the time interval $\pi \le t \le 2\pi$, what is the acceleration of the particle when the velocity is zero?

22. For what values of x is the graph of $y = \ln(1 + x^2)$ concave down?

23.■ Find the average value of the function $f(x) = 2x^2 + 3x + 3$ over the interval $[1, 4]$.

24. ■ The integral to find the volume of revolution when the region bounded by the graph of $y = \sqrt{x}e^{\frac{1}{2}x}$ and the lines $y = 0, x = 0$, and $x = 1$ is rotated about the line $y = -1$ is

(A) $3\pi \int_0^1 xe^{\frac{1}{2}x}\, dx$

(B) $\pi \int_0^1 \left(2\sqrt{x}e^{\frac{1}{2}x} + xe^x \right) dx$

(C) $2\pi \int_0^1 (e-x)\sqrt{x}e^{\frac{1}{2}x}\, dx$

(D) $\pi \int_0^1 \left(\sqrt{x}e^{\frac{1}{2}x} + xe^{x^2} \right) dx$

(E) none of the above

---

25. The range of the function $y = \sin x - \cos x,\ 0 \le x \le \pi$ is

(A) $-1 \le y \le 1$

(B) $-1 \le y \le \sqrt{2}$

(C) $-\dfrac{\sqrt{2}}{2} \le y \le 1$

(D) $-\sqrt{2} \le y \le \sqrt{2}$

(E) $0 \le y \le \sqrt{2}$

---

26. $\displaystyle\lim_{u \to 0} \frac{e^{b+u} - e^b}{u} =$

(A) 0

(B) $\dfrac{1}{e}$

(C) 1

(D) e^b

(E) undefined

---

27. If $y = \sin x$, then

(A) $y' - y = 0$

(B) $y'' + y = 0$

(C) $y'' - y = 0$

(D) $y'' + y' = 0$

(E) $y'' - y' = 0$

---

28. If $f(x) = \ln(x^x)$, then $f'(e^2) =$

(A) 2

(B) 3

(C) $2e$

(D) $3e^2$

(E) none of the above

29. The area bounded by the curve $y = e^x$, the line $y = x$, the y-axis, and the line $x = 1$ is

(A) $e - \dfrac{3}{2}$ (B) $e - 1$ (C) $e - \dfrac{1}{2}$ (D) $e + \dfrac{1}{2}$

(E) none of the above

---

30. Consider the two pairs of definite integrals: $\left\{ P_1 = \displaystyle\int_0^{\frac{\pi}{2}} \cos x\, dx, \quad P_2 = \int_0^{\frac{\pi}{2}} \cos^2 x\, dx \right\}$

and $\left\{ Q_1 = \displaystyle\int_0^{\pi} \cos x\, dx, \quad Q_2 = \int_0^{\pi} \cos^2 x\, dx \right\}$. By inspecting the integrands, which one of the following inequalities is valid?

(A) $P_1 > P_2$ and $Q_1 > Q_2$
(B) $P_1 > P_2$ and $Q_1 < Q_2$
(C) $P_1 < P_2$ and $Q_1 > Q_2$
(D) $P_1 < P_2$ and $Q_1 < Q_2$
(E) none of the above

31.■ A particle is moving clockwise on the ellipse $16x^2 + 4y^2 = 45$. Find all points on the ellipse where $\dfrac{dy}{dt} = -\dfrac{dx}{dt}$.

32.■ Find the area of the region bounded by $f(x) = \dfrac{x}{\sec x}$, the x-axis, and the lines $x = -\dfrac{\pi}{2}$ and $x = \dfrac{\pi}{2}$.

1984

1. If $f(x) = ax + b$ where $f(-3) = 7$ and $f(4) = 5$, then $b =$

   (A) $-\dfrac{43}{7}$ (B) $-\dfrac{25}{6}$ (C) $\dfrac{25}{6}$ (D) $\dfrac{43}{7}$

   (E) none of the above

---

2. Find the values of x at which the curve $y = 6x^2 + x + 5$ crosses the line $y = 6$.

---

3. $\displaystyle\lim_{h \to 0} \dfrac{(3+h)^3 + (3+h) - 30}{h} =$

   (A) -30 (B) 0 (C) 28 (D) 33

   (E) none of the above

---

4. Find the range of the function $f(x) = \sqrt{-x^2 + 2x + 15}$.

---

5. The graph of $f(x) = \dfrac{x^2 - 4}{x^3 + 3x^2 - 4x - 12}$ has a vertical asymptote at $x =$

   (A) -3 only   (B) -2 only   (C) 2 only   (D) 3 only

   (E) $-3, -2,$ and 2

---

6. If $f(x) = \left[\dfrac{x-1}{x+1}\right]^2$, then, for $x \neq 0$ and $x \neq -1$, $f\left(\dfrac{1}{x}\right) =$

   (A) $f(x)$ (B) $-f(x)$ (C) $f(-x)$ (D) $f^{-1}(x)$

   (E) none of the above

7.■ For what values of x is the curve defined by $y = \dfrac{x}{3} + 2 + \dfrac{3}{x}$ concave down?

---

8. ∎ Two tangent lines can be drawn to the curve $y = x^2 + x + 2$ from the point (4, 13). Find the slopes of these two tangent lines.

---

9. Find $\lim\limits_{x \to \frac{\pi}{2}} \dfrac{2x - \pi}{x - \dfrac{\pi}{2}}$.

---

10. If $f(x)$ and $g(x)$ are differentiable functions and $f(3) = 5$, $f'(3) = -7$, $g(3) = -1$, and $g'(3) = 4$, find the derivative of fg at $x = 3$.

---

11. The slope of the tangent to the curve $3x^2 y + y^3 - x^2 = 75$ at the point where $x = 1$ is

(A) $-\dfrac{2}{3}$ (B) $-\dfrac{22}{51}$ (C) $\dfrac{22}{51}$ (D) $\dfrac{2}{3}$

(E) none of the above

---

12. The curve $y = 3x^5 - 5x^4 + 3x - 2$ has a point of inflection at

(A) $(-1, -13)$ only   (B) $(0, -2)$ only
(C) $(1, -1)$ only   (D) $(1, -1)$ and $(0, -2)$
(E) none of the above

---

13. The area bounded by the curves $y = \sqrt[m]{x}$ and $y = x^m$ (where m is a positive integer) is

(A) m (B) $2m + 1$ (C) $\dfrac{m+1}{m-1}$ (D) $\dfrac{m-1}{m+1}$

(E) none of the above

---

14. The graph of $y = \dfrac{ax + b}{(x-1)(x-4)}$ has a horizontal tangent at the point $(2, -1)$. Find a and b.

15. ▪ A particle is moving on the x-axis in such a way that at time t its acceleration is $6t$ inches per second per second. When $t = 1$ the particle's distance from the origin is 10 inches; and when $t = 2$ the distance is 80 inches. Find the velocity with which the particle is moving when $t = 3$.

16. ▪

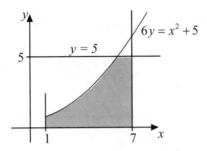

The shaded region in the figure above is bounded by the parabola $6y = x^2 + 5$ and the segments of the straight lines $y = 0$, $x = 1$, $y = 5$, and $x = 7$. Find the area of that region.

17. $f(x) = \dfrac{1 - e^{2x}}{1 - e^x}$. What value must be assigned to $f(x)$ at $x = 0$ to make $f(x)$ continuous at $x = 0$?

18. If $f(x) = \ln(x + 1)$ and $g(x) = \cos 2x$, find the maximum value of $f\big(g(x)\big)$ over the interval $0 \le x \le \dfrac{\pi}{2}$.

19. The range of the function $y = \left(\dfrac{1}{2}\right)^{\sec x}$ is

(A) $y < 0$ 　　　　　　　(B) $y > 0$ 　　　　　　　(C) $0 < y \le \dfrac{1}{2}$

(D) $\left\{0 < y \le \dfrac{1}{2}\right\} \cup \{y \ge 2\}$ 　　　(E) all real numbers

20. If $f(g(x)) = x$ and $f'(x) = \dfrac{1}{x}$, where $f(x)$ contains the point $(1, 0)$, then $g'(x) =$

(A) x (B) $\dfrac{1}{x}$ (C) $-\dfrac{1}{x^2}$ (D) $\ln x$ (E) e^x

21. If $u = \sqrt{x^2 + 16}$ and $v = x^2 + x$, the rate of change of u with respect to v at $x = 3$ is

(A) $\dfrac{3}{70}$ (B) $\dfrac{3}{35}$ (C) $\dfrac{6}{35}$ (D) $\dfrac{3}{5}$ (E) $\dfrac{35}{3}$

22. If $y = e^{\frac{1}{2}\ln(x^2 - 4x + 7)}$, then $\dfrac{dy}{dx} =$

(A) $e^{\frac{1}{2}\ln(x^2 - 4x + 7)}$ (B) $x - 2$

(C) $\dfrac{1}{\sqrt{x^2 - 4x + 7}}$ (D) $\dfrac{x - 2}{\sqrt{x^2 - 4x + 7}}$

(E) $(2x - 4)e^{\frac{1}{2}\ln(x^2 - 4x + 7)}$

23.■ The area bounded by the curve $y = e^{-x}$ and the lines $y = 0$, $x = 0$, and $x = 10$ is rotated about the x-axis. Which of the following is the best approximation for the volume of the solid of revolution so generated?

(A) 0.78   (B) 1.57   (C) 2.71   (D) 3.15   (E) 6.28

24.■ A spherical tank of radius 4 feet contains water to a depth of one foot. How much water must be added to increase the depth by one foot?

25. The value of $\int_0^{\frac{\pi}{4}} \sin x \cos x \, dx$ is

(A) $\dfrac{1}{8}$ (B) $\dfrac{1}{4}$ (C) $\dfrac{3}{8}$ (D) $\dfrac{1}{2}$

(E) none of the above

26. The maximum value of the function $f(x) = 2xe^{-x}$ is

(A) $\dfrac{2}{e}$ (B) 1   (C) 2   (D) $2e$

(E) none of the above

27. A circle with the center at $(3, 0)$ passes through the point $(-3, 8)$. An equation of the line tangent to the circle at the point $(-3, 8)$ is

(A) $4y + 3x = 41$ (B) $4y - 3x = 41$
(C) $3y - 4x = 36$ (D) $3y + 4x = 36$
(E) none of the above

28. If $\dfrac{dy}{dx} = 2xy^2$ and $y = \dfrac{1}{2}$ when $x = 1$, then when $x = 2$, $y =$

(A) -1 (B) $-\dfrac{1}{4}$ (C) 1   (D) $\dfrac{7}{2}$

(E) none of the above

29. Find the domain of the function $f(x) = \sqrt{3-x} + \arcsin \dfrac{3-2x}{5}$.

30. The region bounded by the *x*-axis and $y = \tan x$ from $x = 0$ to $x = \dfrac{\pi}{3}$ is divided into two regions by the line $x = m$. If the two regions are equal in area, then $m =$

(A) $\dfrac{\pi}{6}$ (B) $\dfrac{2}{3}$ (C) $\dfrac{2\pi}{9}$ (D) $\dfrac{3}{4}$

(E) none of the above

31. ▪ Point $P(p, q)$ lies on the parabola $y = x^2$. O is the origin, and $R(0, r)$ is the point where the perpendicular bisector of $\overline{OP}$ intersects the *y*-axis. Find $\lim\limits_{x \to 0} r$.

32. ▪ The *x*-axis and the graph of $f(x) = x^3 - x$ enclose two regions. Find the length of a side of the equilateral triangle with greatest area that can be placed in one of these two regions. The base of the triangle is on the *x*-axis.

1983

1. If $f(x) = \dfrac{4}{x-1}$ and $g(x) = 2x$, the solution set of $f(g(x)) = g(f(x))$ is

   (A) empty   (B) $\{-3\}$ (C) $\left\{-\dfrac{1}{3}\right\}$ (D) $\left\{\dfrac{1}{3}\right\}$ (E) $\{3\}$

2. $\displaystyle\lim_{h \to 2} \dfrac{h^3 - 2h^2 - h + 2}{h^2 - 4} =$

   (A) 0   (B) $\dfrac{1}{2}$ (C) $\dfrac{3}{4}$ (D) 1   (E) ∞

3. On the surface of Mars, a stone is tossed upward with an initial velocity of 40 ft/sec from a height of 6 feet above the surface of the planet. Its height is given by the polynomial function $H(t) = -6.5t^2 + 40t + 6$, where t is in seconds. How many seconds after the stone is released will it reach its maximum height?

4. If $f(x) = 3x - 12$, then $f^{-1}(x)$ evaluated at 4 is

   (A) $-\dfrac{8}{3}$ (B) 0   (C) $\dfrac{7}{8}$ (D) $\dfrac{16}{3}$ (E) undefined

5. The minimum value of the function $y = 4\sin x + 3$ over the interval $\dfrac{\pi}{6} \le x \le \dfrac{5\pi}{6}$ is

   (A) -1 (B) 1   (C) 3   (D) 5   (E) 7

6.   If $f(x-1)=2x^2-3x+1$, then $f(x+1)$ is

(A) $2x^2+x$ (B) $2x^2-x+1$
(C) $2x^2+5x+3$ (D) $2x^2+8x-6$
(E)   none of the above

7.■   The vertex of the parabola ax^2+bx+c has coordinates $(-2,-6)$ and the
      y-intercept has coordinates $(0,-2)$. Find $a+b+c$.

8.■   Find the inflection point, or points, if any, on the graph of $f(x)=(x+2)^{\frac{3}{5}}-1$.

9.   Find $f(x)$, if $f'(x)=2x-3$ and the graph of $y=f(x)$ contains the point $(2,5)$.

10.   Find the absolute maximum of $y=1-(x-4)^{\frac{2}{3}}$ over the interval $[-1,12]$.

(A) $1-\sqrt[3]{64}$ (B) $1-\sqrt[3]{-25}$ (C)   0
(D)   1   (E)   no absolute maximum

11. $\displaystyle\lim_{x\to2}\frac{\sqrt{3-x}-\sqrt{x-1}}{6-3x}=$

(A) $\dfrac{1}{3}$ (B) $\dfrac{1}{2}$ (C) $\dfrac{2}{3}$ (D)   1   (E) $\dfrac{3}{2}$

12.   If $\displaystyle\lim_{h\to0}\frac{f(x+h)-f(x)}{h}=2x$, then $\displaystyle\lim_{h\to0}\frac{f(x)-f(x-h)}{h}=$

(A) $-x^2$ (B) $-2x$ (C) $2x$ (D) $2x+4$ (E) x^2

13. Find an equation of each line normal to the graph of $y = \dfrac{2x}{x-1}$ and parallel to the line $2x - y + 1 = 0$.

14. The area bounded by the curves $4 - x^2$ and $y = x^2 - 2x$ is

(A) $\dfrac{13}{3}$ (B) $\dfrac{20}{3}$ (C) 9   (D) 15

(E) none of the above

15. ■ A particle moves along the x-axis where its position as a function of time is given by $x = t^3 - 9t^2 + 24t + 5$. Find the total distance the particle travels from $t = 1$ to $t = 5$.

16. ■

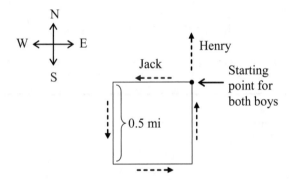

Jack lives at a corner of a square park, $\dfrac{1}{2}$ mile long on each side. Each morning he jogs several times around the park at the rate of 9 miles/hour in a counterclockwise direction, as shown in the figure above. His brother Henry, leaves at the same time as Jack, and walks to school at a rate of 4 miles/hour, due north. At what rate will they be separating $\dfrac{3}{4}$ hour later?

17. $\displaystyle \lim_{x \to -\infty} \dfrac{e^x}{\pi^x} =$

(A) $-\infty$ (B) 0   (C) e (D) π (E) ∞

18. If $y = n^t$, then $\dfrac{d(\ln y)}{dt} =$

    (A) $\ln n$ (B) $t \ln n$ (C) $\dfrac{1}{\ln n}$ (D) $\dfrac{1}{n \ln y}$ (E) $\dfrac{1}{y^n} \dfrac{dy}{dt}$

19. The height of a cone is equal to its radius. Find the rate of change of its volume with respect to the radius.

20. The domain of the function $f(x) = \sqrt{\ln \dfrac{5x - x^2}{4}}$ is

    (A) $x < 0$ (B) $0 < x < 5$ (C) $1 \le x \le 4$
    (D) $x > 0$ (E) all real numbers

21. Find the particular solution of the differential equation $\dfrac{d^2 y}{dx^2} = x - x^2$ with the initial conditions $y' = 0$ and $y = 0$ at $x = 2$.

22. If $x^y = y^x$, then $\dfrac{dy}{dx} =$

    (A) $\dfrac{xe^y - y}{ye^x - x}$ (B) $\dfrac{y^x \ln y}{x^y \ln x}$

    (C) $\dfrac{y(\ln y) - x}{x(\ln x) - y}$ (D) $\dfrac{\ln y - \dfrac{y}{x}}{\ln x - \dfrac{x}{y}}$

    (E) none of the above

23. ■ Find the volume of the solid generated by rotating the region bounded by the graph of $y = x^2$, $y = 0$, $x = 1$, and $x = 3$ about the line parallel to the x-axis and one unit below it.

24.■ Find the coordinates of all points where the curve of $x^2 - xy + y^2 = 1$ has vertical tangents.

25. $\lim\limits_{x \to 0} \dfrac{\tan x - \sin x}{x^3} =$

(A) 0   (B) $\dfrac{1}{4}$ (C) $\dfrac{1}{3}$ (D) $\dfrac{1}{2}$ (E) 1

26. The value of the function $y = 4\ln e^{e^x}$ at $x = 1$ is

(A) 4   (B) $4e$ (C) $8\ln 8$ (D) $4e^e$
(E) none of the above

27. The range of the function $y = \cos(\arcsin x)$ is

(A) $-1 \le y \le 0$ (B) $-1 \le y \le 1$ (C) $0 \le y \le 1$
(D) $0 \le y \le \pi$ (E) all real numbers

28. The graphs of $y = \sin x$ and $y = \cos x$ intersect twice in the interval $0 \le x \le 2\pi$. Find the area of the region bounded by these two curves between the two points of intersection.

29. $\lim\limits_{h \to 0} \dfrac{\sin\left(\dfrac{\pi}{6} + h\right) - \dfrac{1}{2}}{h} =$

(A) 0   (B) $\dfrac{1}{2}$ (C) $\dfrac{\sqrt{2}}{2}$ (D) $\dfrac{\sqrt{3}}{2}$ (E) 1

30.   Find $\displaystyle\int \frac{(x-1)\ln\sqrt{x^2-2x}}{x^2-2x}\,dx$.

31.   Find $\displaystyle\int \tan x\sqrt{\tan x-1}\,\sec^2 x\,dx$.   Hint: let $u=\tan x-1$.

32.   A farmer estimates that if he digs his carrots today, he will have 160 bushels worth two dollars a bushel. If he waits, the crop will increase 40 bushels per week, but the selling price will drop 25¢ per bushel per week. How many weeks from today should he dig his carrots to get the most income?

1982

1. Given $f(x) = x^3 - x$ and $g(x) = \sin 2x$, find $f\left(g\left(\frac{\pi}{12}\right)\right)$.

   (A) $-\dfrac{3}{8}$ (B) $-\dfrac{\sqrt{3}}{8}$ (C) $\dfrac{\sqrt{3}}{8}$ (D) $\dfrac{3}{8}$

   (E) none of the above

---

2. Which of the following functions are neither odd nor even?
   1) $y = x - x^2$ 2) $y = \sin x$ 3) $y = 2^x$

   4) $y = x^4 - 2x^2 + 1$ 5) $y = -\dfrac{x^3}{6} + \dfrac{x^5}{120}$

   (A) 3 only   (B) 4 only   (C) 1 and 3   (D) 1 and 4   (E) 1, 3, and 5

---

3. The equation of the horizontal asymptote for the graph of
   $f(x) = \dfrac{2x^3 - 7x^2 + 8x - 1}{(x-2)(4x-3)(x+1)}$ is

   (A) $y = 0$ (B) $y = \dfrac{1}{2}$ (C) $y = 1$ (D) $x = 2$

   (E) none of the above

---

4. Find $\displaystyle\lim_{h \to 0} \frac{(4+h)^3 + (4+h) - 68}{h}$.

---

5. Find the coordinates of the point of intersection of the line $y = -3x + 10$ and the tangent line to the curve $y = 4 - x^2$ at $x = -1$.

---

6. For the curve $y = 2^{\sin x}$, the range of the function over all real numbers is

(A) $-1 \le y \le 2$ (B) $-\dfrac{1}{2} \le y \le 1$

(C) $-\dfrac{1}{2} \le y \le 2$ (D) $0 \le y \le 2$

(E) $\dfrac{1}{2} \le y \le 2$

7.■ Given $f(x) = \begin{cases} ax + b, & \text{if } x < \dfrac{1}{2} \\ 3x^2, & \text{if } x \ge \dfrac{1}{2} \end{cases}$, find the values of a and b for which this function

is differentiable at $x = \dfrac{1}{2}$.

8.■ For what values of x is the curve $f(x) = \dfrac{1}{x^2 + 1}$ increasing and concave down?

9. Given $f(x) = \dfrac{x}{2} + \dfrac{2}{x}$ over the closed interval $[a, b]$, a value for c such that

$f(b) = f(a) + f'(c)(b - a)$ for $a = \dfrac{1}{2}$ and $b = 4$ is

(A) $-\sqrt{2}$ (B) $-\dfrac{1}{2}$ (C) $\dfrac{1}{2}$ (D) $\sqrt{2}$

(E) none of the above

10. Which of the following is the equation of the normal to the curve
$x^3 + y^2 + 2x - 6 = 0$ at the point where $y = 3$?

(A) $(y+1) = \dfrac{6}{5}(x-3)$ (B) $(y-3) = -\dfrac{5}{6}(x+1)$

(C) $(y+1) = -\dfrac{5}{6}(x-3)$ (D) $y = \dfrac{6}{5}x - \dfrac{23}{5}$

(E) none of the above

---

11. Find the value of $\sin x$ for $\dfrac{\pi}{2} < x < \pi$ where $y = 2\sec x$ intersects $y = \cot x$.

(A) $1 - \sqrt{2}$ (B) $-1 + \sqrt{2}$ (C) $\dfrac{1}{2}$ (D) $\dfrac{\sqrt{3}}{2}$

(E) none of the above

---

12. Consider the curve $f(x) = x^2$ from $x_1 = 0$ to $x_2 = 3$. Find c where $x_1 \le c \le x_2$ such that $f(c)(x_2 - x_1) = \displaystyle\int_{x_1}^{x_2} f(x)\, dx$.

---

13. The graph of $f(x) = \dfrac{x}{x+1}$ over the interval $-2 < x < 2$ has

(A) no asymptotes and no inflection points
(B) no asymptotes and one inflection point
(C) one horizontal asymptote and no vertical asymptotes
(D) one vertical asymptote and no horizontal asymptotes
(E) one horizontal asymptote and one vertical asymptote

---

14. An object is thrown straight down with a speed of 48 feet per second from the edge of a cliff 448 feet high. With what speed will it hit the ground? The acceleration due to gravity is 32 ft/sec^2.

15.■ A balloon was being inflated at the rate of 28 ft³/min, but burst when its volume reached $3\frac{13}{81}\pi$ ft³. At what rate was the radius expanding when the balloon burst? Leave your answer in terms of π.

16.■ The line tangent to the curve $f(x) = 3x^3 - x + 5$ at $x = -1$ intersects the curve only once again. Find the area bounded by this tangent line and the curve.

17. Find the fourth derivative of $y = x^3 \ln x$.

(A) 0   (B) $\dfrac{3}{x}$ (C) $\dfrac{6}{x}$ (D) $\dfrac{12}{x}$

(E) none of the above

18. What is the area of the region bounded by the graphs of $y = \sin x$ and $y = \cos x$ and the lines $x = \dfrac{\pi}{4}$ and $x = \dfrac{5\pi}{4}$?

(A) 0   (B) $\sqrt{2}$ (C) $2\sqrt{2}$ (D) $4\sqrt{2}$
(E) none of the above

19. What is the volume of the solid generated by revolving the area bounded by $y = e^x$, $x = 0$, and $x = 1$ about the x-axis.

(A) $\pi(e-1)$

(B) $\dfrac{\pi}{2}e^2$

(C) $\dfrac{\pi}{2}\left(e^2 - 1\right)$

(D) $\pi\left(e^2 - 1\right)$

(E) none of the above

20. $y = \sqrt{\ln \sqrt{x}}$. $y' =$

(A) $\dfrac{1}{4x}$ (B) $\dfrac{e^x}{4x}$ (C) $\dfrac{1}{4xe^x}$ (D) $\dfrac{4x}{\sqrt{\ln \sqrt{x}}}$ (E) $\dfrac{1}{4x\sqrt{\ln \sqrt{x}}}$

21. Given $(x - y) + \sec^2(x + y) = \tan^2(x + y) + (x + y)$, find $\dfrac{dy}{dx}$ in simplest form.

22. Find the largest subset of the set of real numbers for which the function
$y = \log_{10}\left[1 - \log_{10}(x^2 - 5x + 16)\right]$ is defined.

23.■ Find the dimensions of the rectangle with the greatest area that may be placed with one side on the y-axis and with the vertices of the opposite side lying on the graphs of $y = \pm \ln x$, where $0 < x < 1$.

24.■ Find the numerical value for $\displaystyle\int_0^{\frac{9}{16}} \frac{\sqrt{1 - \sqrt{x}}}{\sqrt{x}}\, dx$.

25. $\displaystyle\lim_{x \to 0} \frac{\sin[2\pi(1 + x)]}{x} =$

    (A) 0   (B) 1   (C) 2π (D) ∞
    (E) none of the above

26. Find the x-coordinate of the point of inflection for the function $y = e^{\arctan x}$.

    (A) -1 (B) $-\dfrac{1}{2}$ (C) $\dfrac{1}{2}$ (D) 1
    (E) none of the above

27. Which of the following is an equation for the normal line to the curve $y = \dfrac{e^x}{x}$ at $(1, e)$?

    (A) $x = 1$ (B) $y = 1$ (C) $x = e$
    (D) $y = e$ (E) $(y - e) = -1(x - 1)$

28. Which of the following represents $\dfrac{dy}{dx}$ if $x = \sec t$ and $y = 1 - \tan^2 t$?

(A) $-2x$ (B) $2x$ (C) $2 \tan t$ (D) $\dfrac{-1}{2 \sec t}$

(E) none of the above

---

29. Find the antiderivative for $\tan x \cdot \ln(\cos x)$.

---

30. $\displaystyle \int_{\frac{\pi}{3}}^{\frac{\pi}{2}} \sin x \cos 2x \, dx =$

(A) $-\dfrac{\sqrt{3}}{4}$ (B) $-\dfrac{5}{12}$ (C) $-\dfrac{1}{12}$ (D) $\dfrac{\sqrt{3}}{4}$ (E) $\dfrac{7}{12}$

31.■ The region bounded by $x = 0$, $y = 0$, and $x + y = 1$ is revolved about the line $y = -1$. Find the volume of this solid of revolution.

32.■ $\displaystyle \int_{0}^{\sqrt{2}} \dfrac{e^{\ln 3x}}{x^4 + 4} \, dx = \dfrac{a\pi}{b}$. Find a and b.

1. The graph of $f(x) = \dfrac{2x^2 - x - 3}{3x^2 - x - 2}$ has a horizontal asymptote which it

   (A) crosses at $x = -5$
   (B) crosses at $x = -\dfrac{2}{3}$
   (C) crosses at $x = \dfrac{2}{3}$
   (D) crosses at $x = 5$
   (E) never intercepts

2. If a function $f(x)$ has symmetry about the origin, then $f'(x)$ has symmetry about

   (A) the origin   (B) the x-axis
   (C) the y-axis   (D) $y = x$
   (E) cannot be determined

3. The line tangent to the curve $f(x) = 2x^4 - 9x + 5$ at $x = 1$ intersects the x-axis at the point

   (A) $(-2, 0)$ (B) $(-1, 0)$ (C) $(0, 1)$ (D) $(1, -2)$ (E) $(2, 0)$

4. A point moves along the x-axis in the positive direction with acceleration of $a = 6t + 2$. The point passes through the origin at $t = 0$ with velocity 3. When $t = 3$, what is the distance between the point and the origin?

5. Find the coordinates of all points on the graph of $4x^2 - xy + 4y^2 = 16$ closest to the origin.

6. What is the domain of the function $f(x) = \ln\left(\ln\left(1 + x^2\right)\right)$?

7.■ Determine coefficients a, b, c, d such that the curve whose equation is $f(x) = ax^3 + bx^2 + cx + d$ has a relative minimum at $(1, 5)$ and an inflection point at $(-1, 21)$.

8.■ Find the area of each of the regions enclosed by the graphs of $y = x$ and $y^3 - y = x$.

9. If a 10 pound force can stretch an 8 inch spring to $8\frac{3}{4}$ inches, how much work will be done in stretching this spring from 8 inches to $9\frac{1}{2}$ inches? Force $F = ks$, where k is a constant and s is the displacement from the normal length. Work is given by $W = \int_0^s F(x)\,dx$.

10. Consider an experiment involving a weight of a radioactive substance whose half-life is 2 days. The amount left at the end of $2N$ days is how many times as great as the amount left at the end of $2N + 6$ days?

11. Find the maximum value of the function $f(x) = 3\cos x - 2\sin x$.

12. Which of the following numbers is the largest? (The arguments in the trigonometric functions are in radians.)

    (A) $\cos 100$ (B) $\log_7 6$ (C) $\tan 1$ (D) $\sin(-17)$ (E) $\left(\sqrt{2}\right)^{\frac{-3}{4}}$

13. Evaluate $\displaystyle\int_{-2}^{2} \frac{dx}{(x+1)^{\frac{2}{3}}}$.

14. A particle moves along the x-axis where its position s at time t is given by $s = t^3 + 3t^2 - 24t + 5$. Find the total distance traveled by the particle from $t = -5$ to $t = 3$.

15.■ There are two lines passing through the point $(3, -1)$ and tangent to the curve $y = x^2 - 4x + 3$. Write an equation for each of these two lines.

16.■ A right circular cone with height 1 has inscribed in it another right circular cone, so that the vertex of the smaller cone is at the center of the base of the larger cone. Find the height of the smaller cone so that it has maximum volume.

17. $\lim\limits_{x \to \infty} \left[e^x \sin e^{-x} \right] =$

    (A) -1 (B) 0 (C) 1 (D) ∞
    (E) none of the above

18. Evaluate $\displaystyle\int_0^{\frac{\pi}{3}} \frac{\sec x \tan x}{1 + \sec^2 x}\, dx$.

19. If $f(x) = x, x \geq 0$ and $g(x) = \ln x, x > 0$, find the natural domain of $f(g(x))$.

    (A) $x > 0$ (B) $x \geq 0$ (C) $x > 1$ (D) $x \geq 1$
    (E) all real numbers

20. $\displaystyle\int_1^7 \sqrt[3]{x^3 - 12x^2 + 48x - 64}\, dx =$

    (A) -7 (B) $-4\frac{1}{2}$ (C) 0 (D) $4\frac{1}{2}$ (E) 6

21. Given the parametric equations $x = \sec\theta$, $y = \tan\theta$, find the rate of change of the slope at $\theta = \dfrac{\pi}{6}$.

22. If $f(x) = e^x \ln x$, what is the approximate value, to the nearest hundredth, of $f(1.01)$ obtained by linear approximation from $f(1)$?

    (A) 0.02   (B) 0.03   (C) 0.04   (D) 0.05   (E) 0.06

23.▪ A chord $\overline{AB}$ of the parabola $y = x^2$, moves toward the vertex at $\dfrac{1}{3}$ unit per second, always assuming positions perpendicular to the axis of symmetry of the parabola. The triangle ABC formed by $\overline{AB}$ and the tangents to the parabola at A and B changes in area because of the motion of $\overline{AB}$. At what rate is this area decreasing at the instant when $\overline{AB}$ is 16 units above the vertex.

24.▪ The region bounded by the parabolas $y = x^2$ and $x = y^2$ is rotated about the y-axis. Find the volume of the solid of revolution generated in this manner.

---

25. Evaluate $\displaystyle\int_0^{\frac{\pi}{3}} \frac{e^{2\ln(\sin x)} + e^{2\ln(\cos x)}}{e^{2\ln(\tan x)} + e^{2\ln 1}}\,dx$.

---

26. Which of the following equations in Cartesian coordinates is equivalent to $r = 4\sin\theta$?

    (A) $x^2 + y^2 - 4x = 0$ (B) $x^2 + y^2 + 4x = 0$
    (C) $x^2 + y^2 - 4y = 0$ (D) $x^2 + y^2 + 4y = 0$
    (E) none of the above

---

27. The line normal to the curve $y = e^x$ at the point $x = -1$ intersects the line $y = x$ at coordinates (p, q). Find p and q.

28. The graph of the pair of parametric equations $x = \frac{1}{2}e^t$ and $y = \frac{1}{2}e^{-t}$ is

   (A) $\frac{1}{4}$ of an ellipse

   (B) an exponential curve
   (C) one continuous section of a hyperbola
   (D) a straight line
   (E) none of the above

29. $\int_{\frac{\sqrt{3}}{3}}^{1} \frac{2x+1}{x^2+1}\,dx =$

   (A) $\ln\frac{3}{2} + \frac{5\pi}{12}$ (B) $\ln\frac{2}{3} + \frac{5\pi}{12}$

   (C) $\ln\frac{3}{2} + \frac{\pi}{12}$ (D) $\ln\frac{2}{3} + \frac{\pi}{12}$

   (E) none of the above

30.

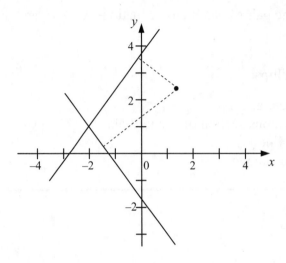

A point moves so that the product of its distances from the lines $4x - 3y + 11 = 0$ and $4x + 3y + 5 = 0$ is $\dfrac{144}{25}$. Which of the following could be an equation of its path?

(A) $\dfrac{(x+2)^2}{9} - \dfrac{(y-1)^2}{16} = 1$ (B) $\dfrac{(x+2)^2}{16} - \dfrac{(y-1)^2}{9} = 1$

(C) $\dfrac{(x+2)^2}{9} + \dfrac{(y-1)^2}{16} = 1$ (D) $\dfrac{(x+2)^2}{9} - \dfrac{(y+1)^2}{16} = 1$

(E)   none of the above

---

31. ■ Find the volume produced when the region bounded by $y^2 = x + 1$, $y = 1$, and $x = 2$ is revolved about the line $x = 2$.

---

32. ■ Find an equation in Cartesian coordinates of the line tangent to
$r = \cos 2\theta$ at $\left(0, \dfrac{\pi}{4}\right)$.

Answers

2004

1. B **2.** D **3.** D **4.** C **5.** C **6.** $\dfrac{1}{2}$ **7.** $a = -\dfrac{3}{2},\, b = -6$ **8.** $a = -\dfrac{1}{4},\, b = d = 0,\, c = 3$ **9.** A

10. C **11.** C **12.** C **13.** A **14.** $(-2, 0)$ **15.** $v = 4$ **16.** $\dfrac{9}{2}$ **17.** B **18.** E **19.** D **20.** D **21.** C

22. $(5, 10)$ **23.** $a = 1,\, b = 0$ **24.** $a = \dfrac{13}{3}$ **25.** C **26.** $\left\{ y \le -\dfrac{e}{\pi^2} \right\} \cup \{ y > 0 \}$ **27.** B **28.** A

29. C **30.** C **31.** $a = \dfrac{\pi}{3}$ **32.** 4

2003

1. B **2.** D **3.** B **4.** A **5.** $k = -4$ **6.** No **7.** See figure below **8.** $c = -12$

9. $\dfrac{1}{2}$ **10.** C **11.** C **12.** D **13.** D **14.** E **15.** $a = 2$ **16.** 36 sec **17.** B

18. A **19.** B **20.** D **21.** $\sqrt{\dfrac{\pi}{2}}$ **22.** D **23.** $y = -4x + 9$ **24.** $k = 1.05$

25. A **26.** A **27.** $x = 1$ **28.** -5 **29.** A **30.** $\dfrac{1}{2}$ **31.** $960\sqrt{10}$ ft

32. $\left(e^2,\, 2 \right)$

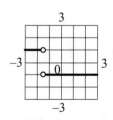

2002

1. E **2.** A **3.** C **4.** C **5.** D **6.** 48 **7.** $\dfrac{375}{12}$ **8.** 23 **9.** A **10.** B **11.** $\left(\sqrt{10},\ \sqrt{10}\right)$ **12.** D

13. C **14.** $v(0) = 12$ **15.** $\dfrac{12}{5}$ units/sec **16.** $9\dfrac{1}{2}$ inches **17.** C **18.** 7 **19.** A **20.** C

21. 1.785 or 4.499 **22.** B **23.** 96 meters **24.** 0.915 **25.** A **26.** $\dfrac{3}{a}\left(b+ax\right)^{\frac{1}{3}}+C$ **27.** A

28. C **29.** $\dfrac{3}{4}$ **30.** D **31.** .376 **32.** .512 lbs/sec

2001

1. A **2.** A **3.** B **4.** B **5.** \$70 **6.** C **7.** $a=\dfrac{4}{3},\ b=\dfrac{8}{27}$ **8.** D **9.** D **10.** D **11.** $v = 9$ units/sec

12. E **13.** D **14.** D **15.** 16 **16.** 15 ft **17.** C **18.** E **19.** A **20.** B **21.** 24 **22.** B **23.** 2.244
24. $60\ln 2$ **25.** E **26.** A **27.** B **28.** D **29.** 52.1 mph **30.** C **31.** 189°F **32.** $\pi\left(e^2+1\right)$

2000

1. C **2.** B **3.** B **4.** C **5.** D **6.** B **7.** $\left(\dfrac{a}{\sqrt{2}},\ \dfrac{b}{\sqrt{2}}\right)$ **8.** $a=2,\ c=-1$ **9.** E **10.** B **11.** $x = 6$

12. −3.167 **13.** B **14.** $2\sqrt{2}$ **15.** 9 sec **16.** 4 million miles **17.** A **18.** C **19.** B **20.** C
21. $\dfrac{1}{2}$ **22.** A **23.** $\dfrac{200}{\pi}$ **24.** 4 ft/sec **25.** A **26.** e **27.** E **28.** B **29.** $26\dfrac{2}{3}\pi$ **30.** B **31.** C
32. $k = -gR^2$

1999

1. 5 ft/sec^2 **2.** C **3.** $-2.915 \le y \le 2.121$ **4.** 73 **5.** E **6.** D **7.** See figure **8.** $a = 1$, $b = 3$, $c = -9$, $d = 10$ **9.** B **10.** B **11.** 24 **12.** B **13.** D **14.** C **15.** 37 ft **16.** 12 **17.** E **18.** A **19.** E **20.** D **21.** D

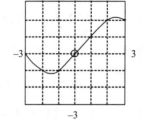

22. $\dfrac{e^2 - e}{3}$ **23.** $\dfrac{1}{2}\left(e^2 - 1\right)$ **24.** $s = 4 \cdot 4^t$; $s(0) = 4$ **25.** E **26.** C

27. $32\dfrac{3}{4}$ **28.** E **29.** $\sqrt[3]{10}$ **30.** 1 **31.** B **32.** 36 sec

1998

1. C **2.** A **3.** D **4.** B **5.** C **6.** A **7.** B **8.** 24 **9.** B **10.** C **11.** B **12.** C **13.** A **14.** $\dfrac{k^2}{2}$

15. $y = 4x$ and $y = -4x$ **16.** $\dfrac{3}{2}$ **17.** A **18.** $\dfrac{-1 + \sqrt{5}}{2}$ **19.** A **20.** B **21.** A **22.** B

23. $d = \dfrac{y_1}{m_1}\sqrt{1 + m_1^{\,2}}$ **24.** 2α **25.** D **26.** E **27.** B **28.** C **29.** B **30.** B

31. 189.434 gallons/hr **32.** 5

1997

1. B **2.** A **3.** A **4.** $c = 3$ **5.** D **6.** E **7.** D **8.** $a = 3$, $b = 9$ **9.** B **10.** D **11.** A **12.** C **13.** B

14. 35,500 ft **15.** $\dfrac{16}{3}$ **16.** 20 mm/sec **17.** $x + \dfrac{4}{5}x^{\frac{5}{4}} + C$ **18.** B **19.** 8 **20.** C **21.** C **22.** A

23. 166.4π lbs **24.** $\dfrac{e^2}{2} + e - 3$ **25.** A **26.** 8 ft/sec **27.** C **28.** D **29.** A **30.** 3 sec **31.** $2\dfrac{1}{12}$

32. $\dfrac{8}{5}\pi$

1996

1. B **2.** A **3.** B **4.** A **5.** c **6.** $200 **7.** $y = \frac{1}{2}x + 1$ and $y = \frac{3}{2}x - 3$ **8.** $a = 3, b = \frac{7}{2}, c = \frac{3}{2}$

9. C **10.** D **11.** B **12.** 10 **13.** $y = -3x$, for $x \le -1$; $y = -x + 2$, for $-1 < x \le 0$;

$y = x + 2$, for $0 < x \le 1$; $y = 3x$, for $1 < x$ **14.** D **15.** $27\sqrt{3}$ **16.** $6\frac{1}{2}$ miles **17.** D **18.** C

19. C **20.** C **21.** 10.6 sec **22.** B **23.** 2 **24.** $400\ln 2$ meters **25.** D **26.** E **27.** D **28.** C

29. $\frac{2}{5}, \frac{2}{3}, 2$ **30.** 36π **31.** $\frac{e^2 + 2e - 5}{2}$ **32.** $t = 30, w = 10.5$

1995

1. A **2.** A **3.** E **4.** A **5.** C **6.** D **7.** -3 and $\frac{1}{3}$ **8.** $-2 < x < 2; x \ne \pm 1$ **9.** C **10.** D

11. $x^3 - 2x + 4$ **12.** E **13.** 1.618 **14.** A **15.** $c = \frac{1}{4}$ and $c = \frac{11}{8}$ **16.** $\frac{3}{4}\sqrt{3}$ **17.** D **18.** A

19. B **20.** D **21.** B **22.** $-\frac{3}{2}\sqrt{3}$ **23.** $\frac{3\pi}{10}$ **24.** $\sqrt{3} - \frac{\pi}{3}$ **25.** 1 **26.** $(\ln 4, 4)$ **27.** D **28.** D

29. C **30.** B **31.** $x = 8m, y = \frac{16m^2 - 1}{4}$ **32.** B

1994

1. B **2.** E **3.** 5120 ft/min **4.** E **5.** C **6.** $-2 \le y \le 2$ **7.** $\frac{7}{4}$ **8.** 12 **9.** D **10.** D **11.** D **12.** C

13. $a = \frac{3}{2}$ **14.** D **15.** $2ks$ **16.** $144,000 **17.** B **18.** E **19.** B **20.** B **21.** A **22.** C

23. $c = \frac{25}{4}$ **24.** $\frac{1}{6}$ **25.** E **26.** $\tan^2 x$ **27.** A **28.** B **29.** $y = \frac{2}{3}(3x^2 + 1)^{\frac{3}{2}} + \frac{1}{3}$ **30.** E

31. $\left(3, \frac{16}{3}\right)$ **32.** $\frac{k}{2}\%$

1993

1. C **2.** B **3.** B **4.** B **5.** A **6.** $\frac{3}{2}$ **7.** 4, 139 **8.** $(3, -4)$ **9.** B **10.** C **11.** B **12.** $(4, 2)$

13. $\left(\frac{1}{2}, \frac{1}{4}\right)$ **14.** E **15.** 8 **16.** $288 **17.** A **18.** C **19.** C **20.** 4 **21.** C **22.** C

23. $a = 3, b = 5$ **24.** 400 miles **25.** $\frac{2}{3}$ **26.** C **27.** D **28.** $\frac{1}{2}$ **29.** C **30.** E **31.** $\pi\left(\ln 2 - \frac{1}{2}\right)$

32. 16%

1992

1. A **2.** $0 \le y \le \frac{5}{2}$ **3.** 40 **4.** C **5.** A **6.** C **7.** $\left(-\frac{3}{2}, -4\right)$ **8.** $a = -3, b = \frac{15}{4}$ **9.** A **10.** 6

11. E **12.** B **13.** D **14.** $c = \frac{2}{3}\sqrt{3} + 1$ and $c = -\frac{2}{3}\sqrt{3} + 1$ **15.** $\frac{50}{3}$ **16.** 0.15 sec **17.** $\frac{1}{2}$

18. C **19.** B **20.** $a - 1$ **21.** $\frac{44}{3}$ **22.** $\frac{e^y}{2 - y}$ **23.** $\frac{12}{25}\pi$ **24.** $\frac{\pi}{6} + \sqrt{3}$ **25.** B **26.** 2 **27.** A

28. B **29.** $\left(\frac{1}{e}\right)^{\frac{1}{e}}$ **30.** E **31.** $\sqrt{3}$ **32.** $\frac{\pi^3}{4} - 2\pi$

1991

1. E **2.** $-20 \le x \le 5$ **3.** D **4.** A **5.** D **6.** $y = 1$ **7.** $a = \frac{1}{6}, k = -\frac{8}{3}$ **8.** $-1 < x < 0$ **9.** B

10. B **11.** $a = 3$ **12.** D **13.** 49 **14.** A **15.** $a = \frac{1}{12}, b = -2$ **16.** $\frac{\pi}{27}$ in/min **17.** C **18.** A

19. $\frac{2}{3}(e^3 - 1)$ **20.** $a = -\frac{1}{2}, b = -3$ **21.** A **22.** A **23.** $(3, 9)$ **24.** 18 meters **25.** $x = e$ **26.** A

27. C **28.** C **29.** B **30.** D **31.** B **32.** $.02

1990

1. D **2.** E **3.** 10 mph/sec **4.** B **5.** B **6.** E **7.** $c = \dfrac{3}{8}$, $d = -6$ **8.** 4 **9.** B **10.** D **11.** E **12.** D

13. $-\dfrac{1}{16}$ **14.** $\dfrac{28}{3}$ **15.** $k = \pm 2$ **16.** $\dfrac{5}{144}$ in/hr **17.** $\dfrac{3}{2}$ **18.** D **19.** C **20.** E **21.** E **22.** 9π

23. 2 **24.** 20 ft/sec **25.** $c = 4$, $d = 1$ **26.** B **27.** B **28.** $\dfrac{1}{6}$ **29.** $\dfrac{e}{2}\cos e$ **30.** $e - 1$

31. $y = e^{\frac{x}{2}}$ **32.** $\dfrac{e^2}{2} + e - \dfrac{5}{2}$

1989

1. D **2.** C **3.** E **4.** C **5.** C **6.** $a = 100$, $b = 90$, $c = 10$, $d = 90$ **7.** $2x^2 + 8x + 8$ **8.** 4

9. $x^3 - x^2 + x - 4$ **10.** 14 **11.** D **12.** C **13.** C **14.** B **15.** 6 in^3/sec

16. $(0, -3)$ and $(-2, -1)$ **17.** E **18.** A **19.** B **20.** $(-1, e)$ **21.** D **22.** A **23.** $a = \dfrac{25}{9}$

24. 36 meters **25.** A **26.** 40° and 320° **27.** A **28.** D **29.** B **30.** $\dfrac{\pi^2}{4}$ **31.** $\sqrt{2}$

32. $\dfrac{5}{3} + 4\ln 4$

1988

1. B **2.** D **3.** A **4.** B **5.** C **6.** C **7.** C

8. $a = -3$, $b = 9$, $c = -\dfrac{1}{2}$ **9.** $c = \sqrt{21}$ **10.** A   **11.** A

12. $(-1, -3)$ **13.** $a = 5$, $b = -3$ **14.** D

15. $(6, 1)$ and $(-54, -9)$ **16.** See figure   **17.** D   **18.** A

19. E **20.** $5K$ **21.** $(2, 2)$

22. $\left(\dfrac{\sqrt{6}}{2}, -\dfrac{1}{2}\right)$, $\left(-\dfrac{\sqrt{6}}{2}, -\dfrac{1}{2}\right)$, $(0, -2)$ **23.** 12   **24.** C

25. D **26.** $\dfrac{1}{2}x^2 + 2$ **27.** E **28.** C **29.** B **30.** E **31.** $\dfrac{1}{2}$

32. 3.2 in/min

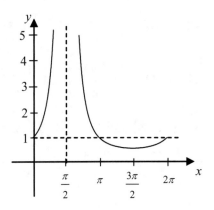

1987

1. E **2.** B **3.** A **4.** A **5.** E **6.** E **7.** D **8.** 3 by $\dfrac{3}{2}\sqrt{3}$ **9.** B **10.** D **11.** B **12.** E **13.** A

14. D **15.** $\dfrac{27}{8}$ **16.** $\dfrac{64}{9}$ **17.** D **18.** A **19.** B **20.** E **21.** $x = -\dfrac{1}{4}$ **22.** B **23.** 63 **24.** 16

25. E **26.** $\dfrac{1}{3}$ **27.** E **28.** 12 **29.** D **30.** 2.98 **31.** $-3e^2$ **32.** $\dfrac{\pi^3}{4}$

1986

1. D **2.** –1 **3.** B **4.** B **5.** A **6.** B **7.** D **8.** (0, 0) and (1, 10) **9.** D **10.** C **11.** B **12.** A

13. E **14.** $-\dfrac{2}{3}$ **15.** 32 in² **16.** 35 ft²/hr **17.** E **18.** A **19.** D **20.** $\dfrac{6}{7}x^{\frac{7}{6}} - \dfrac{4}{3}x^{\frac{3}{4}} + C$ **21.** B

22. A **23.** $\left(\dfrac{1}{e}, \left(\dfrac{1}{e} \right)^{\frac{1}{e}} \right)$ **24.** $\dfrac{104\pi}{5}$ **25.** –3 **26.** B **27.** E **28.** C **29.** 12 **30.** 2π

31. $(-5, 8)$ and $(9, -6)$ **32.** 2π

1985

1. A **2.** D **3.** A **4.** D **5.** –16 **6.** A **7.** $a = 2, b = 2$ **8.** $y = 3x - 5$ and $y = 5x - 4$ **9.** D

10. A **11.** D **12.** B **13.** C **14.** 12 **15.** $a = 40, b = 32$ **16.** $\dfrac{32}{3}$ **17.** A **18.** D **19.** A **20.** C

21. $\sqrt{2}$ **22.** $(-\infty, -1) \cup (1, \infty)$ **23.** $24\dfrac{1}{2}$ **24.** B **25.** B **26.** D **27.** B **28.** B **29.** A **30.** B

31. $\left(\dfrac{3}{4}, 3 \right)$ and $\left(-\dfrac{3}{4}, -3 \right)$ **32.** $\pi - 2$

1984

1. D **2.** $-\dfrac{1}{2}$ and $\dfrac{1}{3}$ **3.** C **4.** $0 \le y \le 4$ **5.** A **6.** A **7.** $x < 0$ **8.** 3 and 15 **9.** 2 **10.** 27 **11.** B

12. C **13.** D **14.** $a = 1, b = 0$ **15.** 90 ft/sec **16.** $20\dfrac{2}{9}$ **17.** 2 **18.** $\ln 2$ **19.** D **20.** E **21.** B

22. D **23.** B **24.** $\dfrac{29\pi}{3}$ **25.** B **26.** A **27.** B **28.** A **29.** $-1 \le x \le 3$ **30.** E **31.** $\dfrac{1}{2}$ **32.** $\dfrac{4}{9}$

1983

1. D **2.** C **3.** $\dfrac{40}{13}$ **4.** D **5.** D **6.** C **7.** 3 **8.** $(-2, -1)$ **9.** $x^2 - 3x + 7$ **10.** D **11.** A **12.** C

13. $y = 2x - 3$ and $y = 2x + 3$ **14.** C **15.** 12 **16.** $\dfrac{169}{\sqrt{173}}$ miles/hour **17.** E **18.** A **19.** πr^2

20. C **21.** $-\dfrac{x^4}{12} + \dfrac{x^3}{6} + \dfrac{2x}{3} - \dfrac{4}{3}$ **22.** D **23.** $\dfrac{986}{15}\pi$ **24.** $\left(\dfrac{2\sqrt{3}}{3}, \dfrac{\sqrt{3}}{3}\right), \left(-\dfrac{2\sqrt{3}}{3}, -\dfrac{\sqrt{3}}{3}\right)$

25. $\dfrac{1}{2}$ **26.** B **27.** C **28.** $2\sqrt{2}$ **29.** D **30.** $\dfrac{\left(\ln\sqrt{x^2 - 2x}\right)^2}{2} + C$

31. $\dfrac{2}{15}(\tan x - 1)^{\frac{3}{2}}\left[3(\tan x - 1)^2 + 5\right] + C$ **32.** 2 weeks

1982

1. A **2.** C **3.** B **4.** 49 **5.** $(1, 7)$ **6.** E **7.** $a = 3, b = -\dfrac{3}{4}$ **8.** $-\dfrac{\sqrt{3}}{3} < x < 0$ **9.** D **10.** E **11.** B

12. $\sqrt{3}$ **13.** E **14.** 176 ft/sec **15.** $\dfrac{63}{16\pi}$ ft/min **16.** $\dfrac{81}{4}$ **17.** C **18.** C **19.** C **20.** E **21.** 0

22. $2 < x < 3$ **23.** $\dfrac{1}{e}$ by 2 **24.** $\dfrac{7}{6}$ **25.** C **26.** C **27.** A **28.** A **29.** $-\dfrac{[\ln(\cos x)]^2}{2} + C$

30. B **31.** $\dfrac{4\pi}{3}$ **32.** $a = 3, b = 16$

1981

1. A **2.** C **3.** B **4.** 45 **5.** $\left(\dfrac{4}{3}, -\dfrac{4}{3}\right)$ and $\left(-\dfrac{4}{3}, \dfrac{4}{3}\right)$ **6.** $x \neq 0$ **7.** $a = 1,\ b = 3,\ c = -9,\ d = 10$

8. 2 **9.** 15 **10.** 8 times **11.** $\sqrt{3}$ **12.** C **13.** $3 + 3\sqrt[3]{3}$ **14.** 128 **15.** $y = -1$ and $y = 4x - 13$

16. $\dfrac{1}{3}$ **17.** C **18.** $\arctan(2) - \dfrac{\pi}{4}$ **19.** D **20.** C **21.** $-3\sqrt{3}$ **22.** B **23.** 4 **24.** $\dfrac{3\pi}{10}$

25. $\dfrac{\pi}{6} + \dfrac{3}{8}$ **26.** C **27.** $p = q = \dfrac{1-e}{e}$ **28.** C **29.** C **30.** A **31.** $\dfrac{8\pi}{3}$ **32.** $y = x$

Index by Topic

Algebra, precalculus, and trigonometry review
Limits
Asymptotes
Definition of derivative
Continuity, differentiability
Differentiation, the Chain Rule
Higher order derivatives
Implicit differentiation
Extrema, concavity, inflection points
Tangent and normal lines
MVT and Rolle's Theorem
Optimization problems
Related rates
Motion problems
Riemann sums
Properties of definite integrals
The Fundamental Theorem of Calculus
Finding antiderivatives and definite integrals
Average value
Areas of regions
Volumes of solids
Differential equations
Parametric curves
Mixed bag

(A graphing calculator is required for those questions marked with a
symbol. No calculator is allowed for other questions.)

Year	Algebra, precalculus, and trig	Limits	Asymptotes	Definition of derivative	Continuity, differentiability	Differentiation, the Chain Rule
2004	2, 26	1	5		7, 10, 11, 17	19, 27
2003	18	1, 9	2	17	6	14
2002	3	1, 9, 17, 25		6, 20		27
2001		1		9	7	2, 4, 13, 27, 30
2000	10		18	4, 9	1	3
1999	3#, 7, 12#	2		9	4	20#, 26
1998	18	1, 9, 19		2, 7		4#
1997	2, 3, 6	1		10	4	9, 12, 18, 21, 22
1996	2, 5, 7, 13	1		3		25, 28
1995	1, 2, 3, 5, 7, 13#, 17	9, 18		4, 12	25	
1994	1, 6, 14, 25, 28	2, 17		11	5, 13, 18	20, 26, 30
1993	2, 3, 9, 26	1, 17, 25	4		6	22
1992	2, 3, 6, 9, 11, 19, 20, 28	1, 17, 25		13	8	18
1991	2, 3, 10, 11	1, 17	6		7, 29	5, 18, 22, 26, 32
1990	2, 18, 27	1, 25	12	4	7	5, 11, 29
1989	7, 18, 22, 26	1, 17	5	4	2	10, 25
1988	2, 3, 5, 14, 16, 17, 25, 26	1, 23	4		13	10, 18, 29
1987	1, 2, 3, 4, 5, 9, 11, 18, 27, 28	19		12, 25		6, 17, 20, 31
1986	1, 4, 9, 13, 18	11, 25		3, 19	2, 22, 27	5, 17, 21, 26
1985	1, 2, 6, 9, 17, 19	3	4	11, 26	15, 18	28
1984	1, 2, 4, 6, 19, 29	9	5	3	17	10, 20, 22
1983	1, 4, 5, 6, 7, 20, 26, 27	2, 11, 17, 25		12, 29		18, 19
1982	1, 2, 6, 11, 22	25	3	4, 21	7	20
1981	6, 10, 12, 19, 26, 30	17	1	2		